Teresa Carrera-Hanley
Rebecca M. Valette
Jean-Paul Valette

Spanish for Mastery 3

Situaciones

CONVERSEMOS
Paired Conversation Activities

Copymasters

D.C. Heath and Company
Lexington, Massachusetts/Toronto, Ontario

Introduction

One of the key goals of **Spanish for Mastery 3:** *SITUACIONES* is to help students build their oral proficiency to the point where they can carry on meaningful conversations in Spanish about various topics relating to everyday life. The *Conversemos:* **Paired Conversation Activities** are designed to help students practice their growing oral skills in a variety of realistic situations. These paired activities provide students with additional opportunities to conduct conversational exchanges in Spanish. In playing the roles, students improve their listening and speaking skills. They find they can express themselves by recombining the structures and vocabulary they have been learning in the current unit with the material they have mastered in previous units.

Although many third- and fourth-year Spanish students welcome the opportunity to express themselves orally and take on new creative conversational roles, some students are reluctant to talk because they do not know exactly what they are to say or how they can best say it using the language at their disposal. To meet this need, the *Conversemos:* **Paired Conversation Activities** provide students with useful conversational prompts and put in their hands a list of topical words and phrases that they can use to express their ideas idiomatically.

Description of the activities

There are 5 conversations to accompany each of the 14 units of **SPANISH FOR MASTERY 3:** *SITUACIONES.* For each conversation there are 2 conversation cue sheets: one sheet for Student A **(Estudiante A)** and one sheet for Student B **(Estudiante B)**. The activity booklet thus contains 70 conversations presented in 140 conversation cue sheets.

Each conversation cue sheet consists of 5 sections:

- *Situación*
  This is a brief description of the conversational situation.

- *Papeles*
  This gives the names of the two speakers and their relationship.
  NOTE: Students A and B both see the same description.

- *Conversación*
  In this section, Students A and B each receive specific instructions as to how to conduct their part of the conversation. Student A always begins the exchange.

- *Sugerencias*
  Here Students A and B are each offered several sample phrases to help them get their conversation started quickly and efficiently.

■ *Palabras y frases útiles*

This is a thematic listing of selected words and expressions that relate to the topic of the conversation. Whereas stronger students may not need to refer to this section, less able students will benefit from this additional conversational support and will profit from the extra guidance. For some conversations, this section is identical for Students A and B; for others, each student may have somewhat different listings.

Using the activities in class

The conversation activities may be incorporated at any point in the lesson plan. You may wish to implement them during the first ten minutes of class as a warm-up activity or to use them in the last ten minutes of class as a recombination activity. Before you hand out the conversation sheets, have students count off in pairs: A, B, A, B, and so on. Then give students "A" the sheets marked **Estudiante A**, and give students "B" those marked **Estudiante B**. Let students quickly read the description of their roles, and then have them start talking. If some students finish early, have them switch roles and carry out a second similar conversation.

While the pairs are talking, walk around the classroom listening to the conversations. If you notice that some students are having difficulty with specific structures or expressions, make a mental note of their problems. When the conversation activity is finished, you may want to go over some of these areas of concern, especially those which interfere with effective communication.

Follow-up activities

Although it is unnecessary to provide a follow-up to each conversation, you may want to consider some of the following suggestions.

1. At the end of a full-class conversation activity, ask for pairs of volunteers to perform their conversation for the entire class. You may want to grant these volunteers some "bonus points" for their contribution.

2. Some more creative students may wish to generate similar conversations on their own by modifying the scenes and/or the roles. Have them present these new dialogues to the entire class as brief skits.

3. After each unit, ask five pairs of volunteers to each prepare one of the conversations, using props and costumes where appropriate. Have students videotape their dialogues and then ask them to share their videos with the entire class. Do similar tapings at the end of each unit so that, in the course of the term, all students have the opportunity to perform. If you are using Portfolio Assessment, you may want to keep these videos as part of the students' oral portfolios.

4. In the course of the year, select the best taped conversations and make a short composite video that you can show to other classes or use on parents' night.

Unidad 1
Situación 1

Estudiante A

Situación

Carlos, a Venezuelan tourist, is in the Café Terraza in Madrid. He starts a conversation with Claudia, another customer, to find out where he can see a flamenco show tonight.

Papeles

➜ **Carlos** *(turista)*
  Claudia *(cliente)*

Conversación

You are Carlos. Start the conversation by introducing yourself to Claudia, who is seated at the next table. Ask her some questions about places where you can see a flamenco show. Find out if she knows where El Andaluz, a popular *teatro-restaurante*, is located.

Sugerencias

— *Por favor, soy turista venezolano.*
   Me llamo Carlos . . .
— *Me gustaría ver un . . .*

Palabras y frases útiles

- *un turista*
- *un lugar*
- *un show flamenco*
- *esta noche*
- *presentarse*
- *llamarse*
- *asistir a*
- *¿puede decirme . . . ?*
- *¿sabe Ud. dónde está . . . ?*

Unidad 1

Situación 1

Situación

Carlos, a Venezuelan tourist, is in the Café Terraza in Madrid. He starts a conversation with Claudia, another customer, to find out where he can see a flamenco show tonight.

Papeles

Carlos *(turista)*
→ **Claudia** *(cliente)*

Conversación

You are Claudia. Respond to Carlos by introducing yourself. Carlos asks you for information about places to go to see flamenco dancing. Let him know that there are three places he can go. Tell him that El Andaluz is near the café where you are eating but that it is very expensive.

Sugerencias

— *Soy Claudia . . .*
— *Conozco tres . . .*
— *Uno es muy caro pero . . .*

Palabras y frases útiles

- *un teatro*
- *un restaurante*
- *un show flamenco*
- *encantado*
- *con mucho gusto*
- *muy caro*
- *cerca de aquí*
- *presentarse*
- *llamarse*
- *comer*
- *bailar*
- *conocer*

© D.C. Heath and Company

Unidad 1

Situación 2

Situación

Luis Alberto and Clara are at their tenth high school reunion. Ana Soriano, a former classmate and well-known movie star, arrives. Luis Alberto and Clara discuss their famous classmate.

Papeles

→ **Luis Alberto**
Clara
(dos amigos)

Conversación

You are Luis Alberto and you begin the conversation by telling Clara that Ana Soriano is the star of *Costa Brava*, an excellent new film. Describe to Clara how Ana's appearance has changed from the time she was in your Spanish class. Tell Clara how Ana used to look and dress.

Sugerencias

— *¿Sabes que Ana Soriano es la estrella de una película muy buena que se llama . . . ?*

Palabras y frases útiles

- *la actriz principal de*
- *una película excelente*
- *la apariencia general*
- *cualidades físicas:*
      (pelirrojo, rizado, etc.)
- *ser*
- *cambiar de apariencia*
- *tener*
- *vestirse*

Unidad 1

Situación 2

Situación

Luis Alberto and Clara are at their tenth high school reunion. Ana Soriano, a former classmate and well-known movie star, arrives. Luis Alberto and Clara discuss their famous classmate.

Papeles

Luis Alberto
→ **Clara**
   (dos amigos)

Conversación

You are Clara. Tell Luis Alberto, who is talking about Ana, that you like Ana's new film. Let him know that Ana was in two of your classes and that you thought she was very pretty then. Inform him that Ana married your cousin and that they have a three-year-old son with curly red hair.

Sugerencias

— *Bueno, Ana Soriano era mi compañera en la clase de . . .*
— *Está casada con mi primo . . .*

Palabras y frases útiles

- *la nueva película*
- *una compañera de clase*
- *la apariencia general*
- *cualidades físicas:*
     (pelirrojo, rizado, etc.)
- *un primo*
- *un hijo*
- *cambiar*
- *tener*
- *vestirse bien*
- *casarse con*
- *estar casada con*

Unidad 1

Situación 3

Estudiante A

Situación

Felipe León, a reporter for *La Vida Diaria* magazine, is conducting a phone survey. He plans to write an article on people's physical appearance and self-image. Felipe interviews Emilio López, a college student.

Papeles

→ **Felipe** *(reportero)*
Emilio *(estudiante)*

— Conversación —

You are Felipe. You call Emilio to find out about his physical appearance and his self-image. Ask Emilio questions to elicit a detailed self-description: shape of face, type of hair, particular traits, etc. Ask him if he considers himself handsome.

Sugerencias

— *¿Puedo hablar con Emilio López?*
— *Ah, con mucho gusto. Soy un reportero de* La Vida Diaria *y me gustaría hacerle unas preguntas.*

Palabras y frases útiles

- *el autorretrato*
- *la apariencia general*
- *estatura*
- *el tipo de cara*
- *las señas particulares*
- *¿cómo es . . . ?*
- *¿qué tipo de pelo tiene?*
- *tener pecas*
- *tener cicatriz*
- *tener lunar*
- *llevar anteojos*
- *llevar lentes de contacto*
- *ser guapo*

Unidad 1

Estudiante B

Situación 3

~~~~~~

Situación

Felipe León, a reporter for *La Vida Diaria* magazine, is conducting a phone survey. He plans to write an article on people's physical appearance and self-image. Felipe interviews Emilio López, a college student.

Papeles

Felipe *(reportero)*
➜ **Emilio** *(estudiante)*

Conversación

You are Emilio. Felipe León calls you to find out about your physical appearance and self-image. Respond to Felipe by describing yourself (shape of face, type of hair, particular traits, etc.). Tell him that you consider yourself fairly handsome.

Sugerencias

— *Sí, soy Emilio López.*
— *Claro que sí, puedo contestarle sus preguntas. Soy . . .*
— *Mi cara es . . .*
— *Tengo el pelo . . .*
— *Soy de estatura . . .*
— *Tengo . . .*
— *Llevo . . .*
— *Creo que soy bastante guapo.*

Palabras y frases útiles

- *la apariencia general*
- *estatura*
- *el tipo de cara*
- *los ojos*
- *las señas particulares*
- *tener pecas*
- *tener cicatriz*
- *tener lunar*
- *llevar anteojos*
- *llevar lentes de contacto*
- *ser delgado*
- *ser esbelto*
- *ser guapo*

© D.C. Heath and Company

Unidad 1

Situación 4

Situación

María Inés is in a bus station when she realizes that she has lost her wallet containing all her personal identification papers. She goes to the lost-and-found booth immediately to report her loss.

Papeles

➔ **María Inés** *(estudiante)*
el Sr. Cortez *(empleado)*

Conversación

You are María Inés. You are talking to Mr. Cortez, the clerk at the lost-and-found booth. Tell him that you have lost your wallet and describe to him the documents that were in it. Provide him with the personal information that the lost documents contained. Ask him to call you at home if the wallet shows up.

Sugerencias

— *Disculpe señor, soy María Inés . . .*
— *He perdido mi billetera . . .*

Palabras y frases útiles

- *la oficina de objetos perdidos*
- *el domicilio*
- *el número de teléfono*
- *una tarjeta de identidad*
- *un carnet de conducir*
- *un carnet estudiantil*
- *la tarjeta de seguridad social*
- *las tarjetas de crédito*
- *la tarjeta de teléfono*
- *perder la billetera*
- *dar los datos personales*

Unidad 1

Situación 4

Situación

María Inés is in a bus station when she realizes that she has lost her wallet containing all her personal identification papers. She goes to the lost-and-found booth immediately to report her loss.

Papeles

María Inés *(estudiante)*
➜ **el Sr. Cortez** *(empleado)*

Conversación

You are Mr. Cortez, the clerk at the lost-and-found booth. You are talking to María Inés, who has lost her wallet. She describes to you the documents that were in her wallet. Ask her all the personal information (name, address, phone number, etc.) you will need to know in case the wallet shows up.

Sugerencias

— *Sí, Srta., ¿en qué puedo servirle . . . ?*
— *Ah, qué lástima.*
— *Puede Ud. darme la información . . .*

Palabras y frases útiles

- *la billetera*
- *el domicilio*
- *el número de teléfono*
- *una tarjeta de identidad*
- *un carnet de conducir*
- *un carnet estudiantil*
- *la tarjeta de seguridad social*
- *las tarjetas de crédito*
- *la tarjeta de teléfono*
- *perder la billetera*
- *dar los datos personales*
- *llamar por teléfono*

Unidad 1
Situación 5

Estudiante A

~~~~~~

Situación

Mr. Valdés, the uncle of Sarita's Spanish pen pal, is visiting the United States and will be staying with Sarita's family for four days. Sarita plans to pick Mr. Valdés up at the train station. She calls Mr. Valdés and suggests that they describe themselves so they will be able to recognize each other at the station.

Papeles

➡ **Sarita** *(estudiante)*
el Sr. Valdés *(invitado)*

Conversación

You are Sarita. You phone Mr. Valdés to tell him you will be waiting for him at the train station. Describe yourself, and ask him to describe himself.

Sugerencias

— *Aló, Sr. Valdés.*

— *Soy Sarita.*

— *Es un placer hablar con Ud.*

— *Lo llamo para decirle que lo voy a esperar en la estación de tren.*

— *¿Puede darme sus señas particulares para reconocerlo?*

Palabras y frases útiles

- *es fácil de reconocerme*
- *voy a recogerlo*
- *ser mediana de estatura*
- *ser delgada*
- *rubia*
- *tener el pelo liso y largo en una cola de caballo*
- *llevar gafas*

Unidad 1

Estudiante B

Situación 5

Situación

Mr. Valdés, the uncle of Sarita's Spanish pen pal, is visiting the United States and will be staying with Sarita's family for four days. Sarita plans to pick Mr. Valdés up at the train station. She calls Mr. Valdés and suggests that they describe themselves so they will be able to recognize each other at the station.

Papeles

Sarita *(estudiante)*
→ **el Sr. Valdés** *(invitado)*

Conversación

You are Mr. Valdés. Sarita calls you to make arrangements to meet you at the train station. Describe yourself to Sarita. Mention two things you will be carrying.

Sugerencias

— *Hola, Sarita.*

— *¿Cómo está?*

— *Gracias por la invitación. Va a poder reconocerme fácilmente porque . . .*

Palabras y frases útiles

- *reconocer*
- *identificar*
- *llevar*
- *un paraguas rojo*
- *un libro en la mano*
- *ser alto*
- *ser grueso*
- *moreno*
- *ser calvo*
- *tener bigotes*
- *llevar anteojos*
- *tener unos . . . años de edad*
- *ser abogado*

Unidad 2

Situación 1

Situación

Miguel has a sister who spends a lot of time in the bathroom every morning getting ready. Miguel finds this extremely annoying and is complaining to Antonio about it.

Papeles

➜ **Miguel**
Antonio
(dos amigos)

Conversación

You are Miguel. You begin the conversation by telling Antonio that your sister spends at least an hour in the bathroom every morning. Tell him that she drives you crazy. Antonio will respond by telling you how annoying his older brother is. Brainstorm to find a solution to your problems.

Sugerencias

— *Antonio, me vuelvo loco todas las mañanas porque mi hermana pasa una hora en el . . .*

Palabras y frases útiles

- *enojarse*
- *hacer cola*
- *volverse loco*
- *levantarse*
- *arreglarse*
- *bañarse*
- *cepillarse los dientes*
- *secarse*
- *peinarse*

Unidad 2

Situación 1

Situación

Miguel has a sister who spends a lot of time in the bathroom every morning getting ready. Miguel finds this extremely annoying and is complaining to Antonio about it.

Papeles

Miguel
➡ **Antonio**
    (dos amigos)

Conversación

You are Antonio. You tell Miguel that your brother also takes over the bathroom in the morning. Tell him how annoying your older brother is. Discuss the best solution to this problem.

Sugerencias

— *¡Qué coincidencia!*
— *Mi hermano hace la misma cosa.*
— *Todas las mañanas . . .*

Palabras y frases útiles

- *enojarse*
- *hacer cola*
- *volverse loco*
- *pasar una hora en el baño*
- *levantarse*
- *arreglarse*
- *bañarse*
- *cepillarse los dientes*
- *secarse*
- *peinarse*
- *marcharse*

Unidad 2

Situación 2

~~~~~~

Situación

Alfredo Pérez is a hotel guest. He realizes that he has forgotten his toiletry kit and calls the hotel receptionist, Mr. Rosas, to ask where he can get a toothbrush, toothpaste, a razor, and deodorant.

Papeles

→ **Alfredo Pérez** *(cliente)*
Enrique Rosas
(recepcionista)

Conversación

You are Alfredo Pérez. You phone the receptionist and identify yourself as a hotel guest. Explain that you have forgotten your toiletry kit. Ask him where you can buy a toothbrush, toothpaste, a razor, and deodorant.

Sugerencias

— *Soy el señor Pérez del cuarto 208.*
— *Olvidé mi bolsa de efectos personales.*
— *¿Puede decirme dónde puedo comprar unas cosas para el arreglo personal?*

Palabras y frases útiles

- *la bolsa de efectos personales*
- *unos artículos para el arreglo personal:*
  - *un cepillo de dientes*
  - *la pasta dentífrica*
  - *una hoja de afeitar*
  - *el desodorante*
- *disculpe la molestia*
- *hágame el favor de . . .*
- *preguntar*
- *olvidar*
- *necesitar*
- *comprar*
- *encontrar*

Situación

Alfredo Pérez is a hotel guest. He realizes that he has forgotten his toiletry kit and calls the hotel receptionist, Mr. Rosas, to ask where he can get a toothbrush, toothpaste, a razor, and deodorant.

Papeles

Alfredo Pérez *(cliente)*

➡ **Enrique Rosas**
(recepcionista)

Conversación

You are Enrique Rosas, the hotel receptionist. Mr. Pérez, a hotel guest, phones you because he forgot his toiletry kit. Inform him that there is a gift shop at the hotel where he can buy a toothbrush, toothpaste, a razor, deodorant, and other personal items. Tell him the hours the gift shop is open and where it is located relative to the front desk.

Sugerencias

— *Lo siento mucho, Sr. Pérez.*
— *Ud. puede solucionar ese problema muy fácilmente.*
— *En el hotel tenemos una tienda . . .*
— *Se abre de . . .*

Palabras y frases útiles

- *la bolsa de efectos personales*
- *unos artículos para el arreglo personal*
- *un cepillo de dientes*
- *la pasta dentífrica*
- *una hoja de afeitar*
- *el desodorante*
- *la tienda queda . . .*
- *olvidar*
- *solucionar el problema*
- *comprar*
- *encontrar*

Unidad 2

Situación 3

Situación

María is studying for tomorrow's important math test. She is exhausted and decides to go to bed; she will get up early. Unfortunately her alarm clock is broken. María asks her brother Carlos to wake her up at 5:00 a.m. so she can study and get ready for school.

Papeles

➜ **María**
  Carlos
  (dos hermanos)

Conversación

You are María. Ask your brother Carlos to wake you up at 5:00 a.m. Explain to him that you need to study for your math test, to get ready, and have breakfast before going to school. Mention how much time you are going to spend doing each of these things.

Sugerencias

— *Carlos, mi despertador no funciona.*

— *¿Puedes hacerme el favor de despertarme a las . . .*

Palabras y frases útiles

- *hacer un favor*
- *tomar el desayuno*
- *tener despertador*
- *tener que madrugar*
- *prestar algo*
- *unas acciones de rutina:*
    - *despertarse*
    - *arreglarse*
    - *comer*
    - *desayunarse*
    - *irse*
    - *levantarse*

Unidad 2

Situación 3

Situación

María is studying for tomorrow's important math test. She is exhausted and decides to go to bed; she will get up early. Unfortunately her alarm clock is broken. María asks her brother Carlos to wake her up at 5:00 a.m. so she can study and get ready for school.

Papeles

María
→ **Carlos**
    (dos hermanos)

Conversación

You are Carlos. Your sister María's alarm clock is broken, and she asks you to wake her up at 5:00 a.m. Explain to her that you need to get up at 7:00 a.m. Ask her to wake you up then. Tell her that she should buy a new alarm clock.

Sugerencias

— *María, ¿puedes levantarme a las . . . ?*
— *Es importante que compres un . . .*

Palabras y frases útiles

- *tener un despertador que no funciona*
- *despertarse a las siete de la mañana*
- *tener que levantarse*
- *prestarle el despertador*
- *comprar un despertador nuevo*

Unidad 2

Situación 4

Situación

Celinda is going to spend three months in Spain as an exchange student this summer. She needs to buy some toiletries. She asks her friend Marcela for advice about what to bring.

Papeles

→ **Celinda**
  Marcela
  (dos amigas)

Conversación

You are Celinda and you ask Marcela what toiletry articles you need to buy to take on your trip. Inform her that there are some items on sale this week. Create a list of items that you both think are necessary.

Sugerencias

— *Antes de irme a España, tengo que comprar . . .*
— *¿Puedes . . . ?*

Palabras y frases útiles

• *unos efectos personales:*
  – *el champú*
  – *la crema*
  – *el desodorante*
  – *la pasta dentífrica*
  – *la laca para el cabello*
• *arreglarse*
• *bañarse*
• *maquillarse*
• *peinarse*
• *lavarse el pelo*
• *perfumarse*
• *pintarse*

Unidad 2

Situación 4

Situación

Celinda is going to spend three months in Spain as an exchange student this summer. She needs to buy some toiletries. She asks her friend Marcela for advice about what to bring.

Papeles

Celinda
→ **Marcela**
(dos amigas)

Conversación

You are Marcela. Your friend Celinda asks you what toiletry articles she will need for her trip to Spain. Create a list of items that you both think are necessary. Tell her why you think she should pack these items.

Sugerencias

— *Mira, para empezar, hagamos una lista de lo que debes llevar.*

— *Para verte muy atractiva debes . . .*

— *Para los ojos necesitas . . .*

Palabras y frases útiles

- *el maquillaje*
- *la sombra de ojos*
- *el rimel*
- *el lápiz de labios*
- *el esmalte de uñas*
- *una secadora de pelo*
- *un peine*
- *un cepillo*
- *unos rulos*
- *unas pinzas*
- *unas tijeras*
- *maquillarse*
- *arreglarse*
- *pintarse*
- *peinarse*

Unidad 2

Situación 5

Situación

Marisol has invited her aunt Lilia to her house for the weekend. Aunt Lilia is an early riser and wants to prepare breakfast for her niece. Marisol describes her Saturday morning routine to Aunt Lilia.

Papeles

➡ **Marisol** *(sobrina)*
Lilia *(tía)*

Conversación

You are Marisol. Aunt Lilia has offered to prepare breakfast for you. Tell her that on Saturdays you get up at 9:00 a.m. Explain that you like to take a long shower and that it takes you 30 minutes to get ready in the morning. Tell Aunt Lilia that you would like fruit juice, an egg, two pieces of toast, and maybe some cereal for breakfast.

Sugerencias

— *Gracias tía Lilia.*
— *Para el desayuno me gustaría . . .*
— *Los sábados me levanto . . . y me gusta tomar una ducha . . .*
— *Me toma . . .*

Palabras y frases útiles

• *el desayuno*
• *un huevo*
• *unas tostadas*
• *el cereal*
• *los sábados*
• *despertarme*
• *levantarme*
• *tomar una ducha*
• *arreglarse*
• *alistarse*

Unidad 2

Situación 5

Situación

Marisol has invited her aunt Lilia to her house for the weekend. Aunt Lilia is an early riser and wants to prepare breakfast for her niece. Marisol describes her Saturday morning routine to Aunt Lilia.

Papeles

Marisol *(sobrina)*
→ **Lilia** *(tía)*

Conversación

You are Aunt Lilia. You are going to make breakfast for your niece Marisol. You ask about her Saturday morning routine and tell her about yours. Ask her what time she gets up. Tell her that you take quick showers but that you like to take your time getting ready and having your morning coffee. Ask Marisol if she would like butter and marmalade on the toast you plan to prepare for breakfast. (Mention that you would like to visit a museum tomorrow and invite Marisol to go with you.)

Sugerencias

— *Marisol, dime, ¿a qué hora te despiertas?*
— *Y quiero saber a qué hora te levantas.*
— *Para el desayuno, ¿te gustaría . . . ?*
— *A mi me gusta tomar una ducha corta y . . .*
— *Mañana me encantaría visitar . . .*

Palabras y frases útiles

- *el desayuno*
- *un huevo*
- *unas tostadas*
- *el cereal*
- *los sábados*
- *despertarme*
- *levantarme*
- *tomar una ducha*
- *arreglarse*
- *alistarse*

© D.C. Heath and Company

Unidad 3

Situación 1

Estudiante A

Situación

Silvia is exhausted. She has just spent the afternoon vacuuming, dusting, doing the laundry, and putting it away. Teresa, Silvia's best friend, invites her to go to the movies.

Papeles

→ **Teresa**
Silvia
  (dos amigas)

UNIDAD 3
Situación 1 **A**

Conversación

You are Teresa. You call Silvia to invite her to the movies this evening. Silvia declines the invitation because she is exhausted. She did a lot of chores today. Arrange another time when you can both go to the the movies.

Sugerencias

— *Silvia, ¿qué te parece si vamos al cine esta noche?*
— *En el cine Las Estrellas están dando una película fantástica de Clint Eastwood.*

Palabras y frases útiles

- *la función de esta noche*
- *el actor*
- *la actriz*
- *una película de vaqueros*
- *la taquilla*
- *los billetes agotados*
- *hacer cola*
- *pasar por tu casa*
- *hacer una cita para otro día*

© D.C. Heath and Company

CONVERSEMOS   21

Unidad 3

Situación 1

Situación

Silvia is exhausted. She has just spent the afternoon vacuuming, dusting, doing the laundry, and putting it away. Teresa, Silvia's best friend, invites her to go to the movies.

Papeles

Teresa
➡ **Silvia**
  (dos amigas)

Conversación

You are Silvia. Teresa phones you to invite you to the movies. Politely decline the invitation and tell Teresa why you are exhausted. Choose another day to go to the movies.

Sugerencias

— *Muchas gracias, Teresa.*
— *Me parece una idea fantástica.*
— *Pero, tengo que disculparme.*
— *Estoy rendida porque . . .*
— *¿Puedes . . . ?*

Palabras y frases útiles

- *invitar*
- *estar rendida*
- *acabar de hacer muchos quehaceres*
- *lavar la ropa*
- *planchar*
- *pasar la aspiradora*
- *quitar el polvo*
- *recoger los periódicos*

UNIDAD 3 Situación 1 B

Unidad 3

Estudiante A

Situación 2

Situación

Mr. Morales is telling his son José that they are expecting company this evening. Mr. Morales wants José to clean his room this afternoon.

Papeles

➔ **El Sr. Morales** *(padre)*
José *(hijo)*

UNIDAD 3
Situación 2
A

Conversación

You are Mr. Morales. You begin the conversation by telling José that four people are coming to the house for dinner. Instruct José to clean his room very well. He replies that he is too busy today and that besides, the vacuum cleaner does not work.

Sugerencias

— *Joséee . . . Joséee . . . ¡Mira, hijo!*
— *Esta noche llegan los Buendía, unos amigos que no he visto en muchos años.*
— *Debes limpiar tu cuarto . . .*

Palabras y frases útiles

- *recibir a los invitados*
- *ser nítido*
- *ser organizado*
- *estar ocupadísimo*
- *estar rendido*
- *hacer la cama*
- *recoger la ropa*
- *colgar la ropa*
- *quitar el polvo*
- *arreglar el cuarto*
- *pasar la aspiradora*

Unidad 3

Situación 2

Situación

Mr. Morales is telling his son José that they are expecting company this evening. Mr. Morales wants José to clean his room this afternoon.

Papeles

El Sr. Morales *(padre)*

➡ **José** *(hijo)*

— Conversación —

You are José. Your father tells you that four people are coming to the house for dinner. He wants you to clean your room very well. Tell your father that you are very busy today; you have soccer practice until 6:00 p.m. In addition, the vacuum cleaner does not work. Ask him not to show your room to the guests. Offer to lock your door.

Sugerencias

— *Papá, de veras, no puedo hoy.*
— *Tengo otras cosas que hacer.*
— *Tengo práctica de . . .*
— *Necesito estudiar para . . .*
— *Además, la aspiradora . . .*
— *¿Te parece bien si cierro con llave . . . ?*

Palabras y frases útiles

- *la práctica de fútbol*
- *la aspiradora no funciona*
- *voy a tratar de*
- *estar ocupadísimo*
- *estar rendido*
- *cerrar con llave*
- *unos quehaceres:*
  - *hacer la cama*
  - *recoger la ropa*
  - *colgar la ropa*
  - *quitar el polvo*
  - *arreglar el cuarto*
  - *pasar la aspiradora*

Situación

Mateo is visiting his college friend David. David's room is a mess.

Papeles

➜ **Mateo**
David
(dos amigos)

Conversación

You are Mateo. Talk to David about neatness. Tell him to do his laundry, hang up his clothes, sweep the floor, and dust at least once a week. Help David make a list of chores that will help him keep his room neat.

Sugerencias

— *¡Oye, David! Eres muy desordenado.*
— *Debes arreglar tu cuarto un poco.*
— *¿Por qué no recoges la ropa . . . ?*

Palabras y frases útiles

- *un cuarto desordenado*
- *unos quehaceres*
- *recomendar*
- *sugerir*
- *aconsejar*
- *arreglar*
- *barrer*
- *colgar*
- *lavar*
- *quitar el polvo*
- *recoger la ropa*
- *vaciar el cesto de papeles*

Unidad 3

Situación 3

Situación

Mateo is visiting his college friend David. David's room is a mess.

Papeles

Mateo
➡ **David**
(dos amigos)

Conversación

You are David. Tell Mateo that you are usually a neat person. Give him two good reasons why you have been too busy lately to straighten out your room. Create, with Mateo's help, a list of chores that will help you keep your room neat.

Sugerencias

— *Estoy de acuerdo.*

— *Generalmente . . .*

— *Pero, déjame decirte las razones . . .*

— *Ayúdame a . . .*

Palabras y frases útiles

- *un cuarto desordenado*
- *todos los días*
- *la práctica de deportes*
- *ser bastante ordenado*
- *la aspiradora no funciona*
- *el trapo*
- *tener práctica de deportes*
- *trabajar por las tardes*
- *estar rendido*
- *ser voluntario*
- *colgar*
- *lavar*
- *quitar el polvo*
- *recoger la ropa*
- *vaciar el cesto de papeles*

Situación

Marisa and her family are going away on vacation for a week. Marisa's family is very friendly with Iván, the next door neighbor. Marisa asks Iván to take care of the house while they are away.

Papeles

➜ **Marisa**
Iván
(dos vecinos)

Conversación

You are Marisa. You phone Iván to ask him to take care of the house while you are away. Explain what he has to do: for example, cut the grass, water the plants, take care of the dog, etc.

Sugerencias

— *Iván, te llamo para pedirte un favor.*

— *La próxima semana nos vamos de vacaciones.*

— *¿Podrías hacerme el favor de . . . ?*

Palabras y frases útiles

- *pedir un favor*
- *cuidar la casa*
- *hacer unos quehaceres*
- *unos trabajos:*
  - *cortar la hierba*
  - *regar las plantas*
  - *dar de comer al perro*
  - *sacar a pasear al perro*
  - *recoger el correo*
  - *recoger el periódico*

Unidad 3

Situación 4

Situación

Marisa and her family are going away on vacation for a week. Marisa's family is very friendly with Iván, the next door neighbor. Marisa asks Iván to take care of the house while they are away.

Papeles

Marisa
→ **Iván**
  (dos vecinos)

Conversación

You are Iván. Your neighbor Marisa phones you to ask you to take care of her house while she and her family are on vacation. Make sure you know what you must do. Ask Marisa for some clarification on each of the chores. Ask her if she would be willing to do the same for you during the third week of August.

Sugerencias

— *Con mucho gusto, Marisa.*
— *¿Puedes decirme qué debo hacer?*
— *A propósito, la tercera semana . . .*

Palabras y frases útiles

- *pedir un favor*
- *cuidar la casa*
- *recoger el correo*
- *recoger el periódico*
- *regar las plantas*
- *dar de comer al perro*
- *sacar a pasear al perro*
- *sacar la basura*

Unidad 3

Situación 5

Situación

Bárbara has invited her friend Cristóbal over for dinner, and they have just finished eating. Cristóbal offers to help Bárbara with the dishes.

Papeles

→ **Bárbara**
Cristóbal
(dos amigos)

Conversación

You are Bárbara. You and your friend Cristóbal have just finished eating dinner. Cristóbal volunteers to help you clear the table. Ask him to help you load the dishes into the dishwasher as well.

Sugerencias

— *Si quieres darme una mano, hazme el favor de colocar los platos en el . . .*

— *Seca los . . .*

— *Después . . .*

Palabras y frases útiles

- *dar una mano*
- *me gustaría ayudar un poco*
- *hacer un favor*
- *echar una mano*
- *colocar los platos en el lavaplatos*
- *recoger la mesa*
- *limpiar la mesa*
- *secar los platos*
- *recoger el mantel*
- *lavaplatos*
- *poner los platos en el gabinete*

Unidad 3

Situación 5

Situación

Bárbara has invited her friend Cristóbal over for dinner, and they have just finished eating. Cristóbal offers to help Bárbara with the dishes.

Papeles

Bárbara
→ **Cristóbal**
   (dos amigos)

Conversación

You are Cristóbal, and you have just finished eating dinner at Bárbara's house. Offer to help Bárbara clear the table. Ask her what else you can do to help.

Sugerencias

— *Bárbara, gracias por la exquisita comida . . .*
— *Dime, qué otras cosas debo hacer?*
— *¿Puedo . . . ?*

Palabras y frases útiles

- *dar una mano*
- *me gustaría ayudar un poco*
- *echar una mano*
- *recoger la mesa*
- *colocar los platos en el lavaplatos*
- *secar los cristales a mano*
- *recoger el mantel*
- *colocar los platos en el gabinete*
- *sacar la basura*

Unidad 4

Situación 1

Situación

Vanesa, who lives in Boston, is planning to take the train to Washington, D.C. She needs to leave her car at the train station for the weekend. Vanesa phones the train station for information.

Papeles

➜ **Vanesa** (cliente)
Sebastián (empleado)

Conversación

You are Vanesa and you ask Sebastián, a train station employee, for information. Ask him how to get to the parking lot from the main road. Inquire about the train schedule and ask him from which platform the train departs. Ask him two other questions concerning your trip.

Sugerencias

— *Disculpe, ¿me podría indicar cómo ir al estacionamiento de coches de la estación de tren?*

— *Estoy en . . .*

Palabras y frases útiles

- *podría decirme cómo*
- *hágame el favor de*
- *me puede ayudar*
- *andar*
- *a la derecha*
- *a la izquierda*
- *derecho*
- *el andén*
- *el estacionamiento*
- *el letrero*
- *el semáforo*

UNIDAD 4
Situación 1
A

© D.C. Heath and Company

Unidad 4

Situación 1

Situación

Vanesa, who lives in Boston, is planning to take the train to Washington, D.C. She needs to leave her car at the train station for the weekend. Vanesa phones the train station for information.

Papeles

Vanesa *(cliente)*
→ **Sebastián** *(empleado)*

Conversación

You are Sebastián, and you work at the train station. Tell Vanesa how to get to the parking lot from the main road. Then give her information about the train schedule. Tell her that all the trains to Washington, D.C. leave from platform number 4. Answer any other questions she asks.

Sugerencias

— *Srta., es muy fácil llegar al estacionamiento de coches.*

— *Simplemente vaya derecho por . . .*

— *En el segundo sémaforo, vire a la . . .*

Palabras y frases útiles

- *claro que sí*
- *con mucho gusto*
- *no es difícil de encontrar*
- *andar*
- *virar*
- *parar*
- *a la derecha*
- *a la izquierda*
- *el andén*
- *el estacionamiento*
- *el letrero*
- *el semáforo*

Unidad 4

Situación 2

Situación

Today is Fabián's first day at a new school. He has just moved into the neighborhood, and a classmate named Alejandro has introduced himself. Alejandro asks Fabián what his name is and where he lives.

Papeles

→ **Alejandro**
Fabián
(dos estudiantes)

Conversación

You are Alejandro. You initiate the conversation by introducing yourself to Fabián and welcoming him to the school. Ask Fabián where he lives and how far it is from school. Answer his questions.

Sugerencias

— *Mucho gusto. Me llamo Alejandro . . .*
    y soy . . .
— *¿Cómo te llamas?*
— *¿Eres nuevo . . . ?*
— *¿Vives . . . ?*

Palabras y frases útiles

- *unas señas*
- *al lado de*
- *cerca de*
- *enfrente de*
- *a unos cien metros*
    en la esquina
- *a diez minutos de . . .*
- *cómo ir*
- *cómo llegar*
- *ser nuevo*
- *vivir*
- *conocer*
- *pasar por*

Unidad 4

Situación 2

Situación

Today is Fabián's first day at a new school. He has just moved into the neighborhood, and a classmate named Alejandro has introduced himself. Alejandro asks Fabián what his name is and where he lives.

Papeles

Alejandro
→ **Fabián**
(dos estudiantes)

Conversación

You are Fabián. Alejandro is very friendly and has initiated a conversation with you. Tell him that you moved here a week ago. Tell him where you live and ask him about the best ways to come to school. Make plans to come to school together tomorrow.

Sugerencias

— *Mucho gusto. Soy Fabián . . . y soy el nuevo . . .*

— *Acabo de mudarme hace una semana y todavía no conozco . . .*

— *Mañana . . .*

Palabras y frases útiles

- *unas señas*
- *al lado de*
- *cerca de*
- *enfrente de*
- *a unos cien metros*
- *en la esquina*
- *a diez minutos de . . .*
- *dónde queda*
- *cómo ir*
- *cómo llegar*
- *mudarse*
- *indicar*
- *vivir*
- *conocer*
- *pasar por*
- *tomar el autobús*
- *caminar juntos*

Unidad 4

Situación 3

Situación

Miguel and Esteban are making plans for this afternoon. They live far away from each other and have to meet at a place convenient for both.

Papeles

→ **Miguel**
Esteban
(dos compañeros)

Conversación

You are Miguel and you call your friend Esteban to make plans for this afternoon. Tell Esteban that you should meet at the bus stop across from the post office next to the tourist office at 4:30 p.m., because the movies start at 6:00 p.m. Make some alternate plans in case you miss each other.

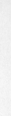

Sugerencias

— *Esteban, debemos encontrarnos cerca de . . .*
— *Si no nos encontramos . . .*

Palabras y frases útiles

- *la oficina de correos*
- *la oficina de turismo*
- *la parada de autobuses*
- *la estatua*
- *hacer planes*
- *encontrarse*
- *tomar un taxi*

Unidad 4

Situación 3

Situación

Miguel and Esteban are making plans for this afternoon. They live far away from each other and have to meet at a place convenient for both.

Papeles

Miguel
➜ **Esteban**
   (dos compañeros)

Conversación

You are Esteban. Miguel phones you about your plans for this afternoon. Tell Miguel about another place besides the bus stop to meet. Suggest that 4:30 p.m. is too early because the movies start at 6:30 p.m. and not at 6:00. Decide with Miguel on an alternate meeting place in case you do not arrive at the original meeting place on time.

Sugerencias

— *Está bien, Esteban, podemos ir a ver esa película.*

— *Pero, por qué no nos encontramos a las 5:30 de la tarde enfrente . . .*

Palabras y frases útiles

- *hacer planes*
- *encontrarse*
- *tomar el metro*
- *tomar un taxi*
- *la oficina de correos*
- *la oficina de turismo*
- *la parada de autobuses*
- *la estatua*

Unidad 4

Situación 4

Situación

Felicia, an Argentinian tourist, is lost in Madrid. She stops Claudio, a pedestrian, to ask directions.

Papeles

→ **Felicia** *(turista)*
Claudio *(peatón)*

Conversación

You are Felicia. You stop Claudio, a pedestrian, and ask him where Génova Street is. Mention to Claudio that you know it is near Hortaleza Street. Explain that you just walked three blocks and you can't find either street. Claudio will give you the necessary directions.

Sugerencias

— ¡Por favor! ¿Podría indicarme dónde queda la calle de Génova . . . ?

Palabras y frases útiles

- ¿podría explicarme dónde queda . . . ?
- estar perdido(a)
- la calle de Génova
- la calle de Hortaleza
- una cuadra
- muy cerca
- encontrar
- hallar
- cruzar
- buscar

Unidad 4

Situación 4

Situación

Felicia, an Argentinian tourist, is lost in Madrid. She stops Claudio, a pedestrian, to ask directions.

Papeles

Felicia *(turista)*
➡ **Claudio** *(peatón)*

Conversación

You are Claudio. Tell Felicia where Génova Street is. Explain to her that Hortaleza Street is at the end of Génova. Tell her to continue straight ahead for three blocks and take a right at the light. Tell her she will see the skyscraper where the insurance company El Águila has its offices. Give Claudia as much help as possible. Make sure your directions are clear.

Sugerencias

— *Con mucho gusto.*
— *Mire, la calle de Génova está bastante cerca.*
— *Camine tres . . .*
— *Luego . . .*
— *Al final de la calle, va a ver . . .*

Palabras y frases útiles

- *déjeme decirle*
- *dónde se encuentra*
- *la calle de Génova*
- *la calle de Hortaleza*
- *la compañía de seguros*
- *una cuadra*
- *un semáforo*
- *muy cerca*
- *a la izquierda*
- *un rascacielos*
- *un letrero*
- *a la derecha*
- *virar*
- *bajar hasta*
- *doblar*
- *parar*
- *ir derecho*

Situación

Today is Sara's first day at her new job and she is not familiar with the building. Víctor, the security guard, gives her directions.

Papeles

→ **Víctor** *(guardia)*
Sara *(empleada nueva)*

Conversación

You are Víctor, one of the security guards. You realize that Sara is new to the building. Ask her where she is going and what department she wants. Indicate to her that the elevator is near the emergency exit sign. Tell her to go to the fifth floor, take a left, and go to the office at the end of the hall. Give her any additional directions necessary to get to her office.

Sugerencias

— *¡Perdón! ¿En qué puedo servirle?*
— *¿Qué oficina busca?*

Palabras y frases útiles

- *¿adónde va?*
- *suba hasta el . . .*
- *tome las escaleras*
- *suba en el ascensor*
- *quinto piso*
- *a la izquierda*
- *al fondo del pasillo*
- *el letrero de salida*
- *la emergencia*

**UNIDAD 4
Situación 5 A**

Situación

Today is Sara's first day at her new job and she is not familiar with the building. Víctor, the security guard, gives her directions.

Papeles

Víctor *(guardia)*
➔ **Sara** *(empleada nueva)*

Conversación

You are Sara and you do not know your way. Víctor, the security guard on duty, asks where you want to go. Tell him that you are looking for the office of Vidal and Vidal and that you are Mr. Vidal's new assistant. Ask him two additional information questions you think are important to know.

Sugerencias

— *¿Puede indicarme dónde se halla la . . . ?*
— *Soy la nueva asistente de . . .*

Palabras y frases útiles

- *disculpe, ¿hágame el favor de . . . ?*
- *me llamo . . .*
- *soy la asistente de . . .*
- *¿dónde puedo estacionar el coche?*
- *¿a qué hora abren las oficinas?*
- *¿hay un ascensor de servicio?*
- *al fondo del pasillo*
- *quinto piso*

Unidad 5

Situación 1

Situación

It is Monday morning, and Simón and his friend Emilia are talking about what they did over the weekend.

Papeles

→ **Simón**
  Emilia
  (dos amigos)

Conversación

You are Simón. Tell Emilia that on Saturday night you went to Roberto's party and danced to modern Latin music. Tell her that you taught the other people there how to dance the salsa. Emilia was supposed to be at the same party; ask her why she didn't go.

Sugerencias

— *¿Emilia, sabes que hice este fin de semana pasado?*
— *El sábado por la noche . . .*

Palabras y frases útiles

- *la fiesta*
- *la salsa*
- *aprender*
- *bailar*
- *escuchar*
- *enseñar el baile*
- *encontrarse*
- *divertirse*

Situación

It is Monday morning, and Simón and his friend Emilia are talking about what they did over the weekend.

Papeles

Simón
➡ **Emilia**
  (dos amigos)

Conversación

You are Emilia. You were supposed to go to Roberto's party Saturday night, but you had to entertain some out-of-town friends that night. Tell Simón that you had a good time; you went out to dinner and to a discotheque. Tell him that you learned two new dances.

Sugerencias

— *¡Qué lástima que no pude ir a la fiesta de Roberto!*

— *Pero, los amigos que me visitaron fueron muy divertidos.*

— *Primero . . .*

— *Y después . . .*

— *Además aprendí . . .*

Palabras y frases útiles

- *aprender*
- *bailar*
- *escuchar*
- *encontrarse*
- *divertirse*
- *entretener a los amigos*
- *aprender un baile nuevo*

Unidad 5

Situación 2

Situación

Susana is a box office clerk. Soledad is a customer waiting in line for tickets to tonight's show.

Papeles

➡ **Susana** *(empleada)*
Soledad *(cliente)*

Conversación

You are Susana and you work as the theater box office clerk. Soledad, a customer, wants to buy tickets for tonight's show. Tell Soledad that you only have the most expensive tickets left. Advise her to buy them right now because you think that all seats will be sold out in an hour.

Sugerencias

— *Lo siento señorita pero nos quedan solamente los billetes más caros.*
— *Le sugiero que . . .*
— *En una hora . . .*

Palabras y frases útiles

- *la función*
- *los billetes de buen precio*
- *más caros*
- *los mejores asientos*
- *lo siento mucho*
- *no puedo venderle*
- *los billetes están agotados*
- *en una hora*
- *quedar*
- *comprar*
- *tener*
- *acabar de . . .*

© D.C. Heath and Company

UNIDAD 5
Situación 2
A

Unidad 5

Situación 2

Situación

Susana is a box office clerk. Soledad is a customer waiting in line for tickets to tonight's show.

Papeles

Susana *(empleada)*
➡ **Soledad** *(cliente)*

Conversación

You are Soledad. You want to buy tickets for tonight's show. Susana, the box office clerk, informs you that only the most expensive tickets are left. Tell her that they are too expensive for you. Ask her if you can have the less expensive tickets for another night. Ask her if there are any special discounts for students.

Sugerencias

— *Son demasiado caros . . .*
— *¿Tiene billetes más baratos para . . . ?*
— *¿Sabe Ud. si hay . . . ?*

Palabras y frases útiles

- *la función del otro día*
- *los billetes*
- *agotados*
- *los descuentos especiales*
- *los descuentos para estudiantes*
- *quedar*
- *comprar*
- *tener asientos*
- *acabar de . . .*
- *ser caros*

Unidad 5

Situación 3

Situación

Rogelio calls his good friend Isabel to ask her to the movies. Isabel's cousins are arriving from Spain tonight and she is unable to go. Rogelio and Isabel discuss the film and plan to go to the movies another night.

Papeles

→ **Rogelio**
Isabel
(dos amigos)

Conversación

You are Rogelio. You invite your friend Isabel to see a movie tonight. When she explains that she is busy tonight, make plans to go to the movies another night.

Sugerencias

— *Isabel, ¿qué tal si vamos al cine esta noche?*

— *Están dando una película fantástica en el Cine Maya y dicen que es muy cómica . . .*

Palabras y frases útiles

• *la ventanilla*
• *la primera sesión*
• *cómica*
• *invitar al cine*
• *ir al cine*
• *empezar*
• *preferir*
• *ver una película*
• *hacer cola*
• *conseguir los billetes*

UNIDAD 5
Situación 3 **A**

Situación

Rogelio calls his good friend Isabel to ask her to the movies. Isabel's cousins are arriving from Spain tonight and she is unable to go. Rogelio and Isabel discuss the film and plan to go to the movies another night.

Papeles

Rogelio
➜ **Isabel**
   (dos amigos)

Conversación

You are Isabel. Your friend Rogelio phones you to invite you to the movies tonight. Excuse yourself by telling Rogelio that your cousins are arriving tonight from Spain. Ask him if you can go another night.

Sugerencias

— *Te lo agradezco mucho.*
— *Hace tres semanas que quiero ver esa película.*
— *Desafortunadamente, esta noche . . .*

Palabras y frases útiles

- *me parece una buena idea*
- *desafortunadamente*
- *es una lástima*
- *otra noche*
- *otro día*
- *llegar de España*
- *empezar*
- *invitar*
- *ir al cine*
- *preferir*
- *ver una película*

Unidad 5

Situación 4

Situación

Lorenzo spent a month in Quito, Ecuador, this summer. While he was there, he attended a well-known tennis tournament. He phones his former Spanish teacher to tell her about his travel experience, and he describes this event.

Papeles

→ **Lorenzo** *(estudiante)*
la Sra. Hernández
(profesora)

Conversación

You are Lorenzo. You phone Mrs. Hernández to tell her that you were in Quito during the month of June. Tell her that you went to see Andrés Gómez play in the Ecuadoran Tennis Cup Tournament. Mention that you were invited to a reception for him at the tennis club and that you also met other tennis celebrities. Mrs. Hernández will ask you questions about your trip.

Sugerencias

— *¿Qué tal? ¿Cómo está, Sra. Hernández?*
— *Acabo de llegar de Quito y quería contarle lo fabuloso que fue mi viaje.*
— *Fui . . .*

Palabras y frases útiles

- *un torneo*
- *la copa*
- *la cancha de tenis*
- *los famosos jugadores de tenis*
- *unos jugadores muy conocidos*
- *pasar un mes*
- *ver un torneo de tenis*
- *jugar al tenis*
- *invitar*
- *ser invitado*
- *participar*

Unidad 5

Situación

Lorenzo spent a month in Quito, Ecuador, this summer. While he was there, he attended a well-known tennis tournament. He phones his former Spanish teacher to tell her about his travel experience, and he describes this event.

Papeles

Lorenzo *(estudiante)*

→ **la Sra. Hernández** *(profesora)*

Conversación

You are Mrs. Hernández. Lorenzo, a former student, phones you to tell you about his trip to Quito. He tells you about the Ecuadoran Tennis Cup Tournament and the reception for Andrés Gómez. Ask him five questions about his trip.

Sugerencias

— *Me alegro mucho de que te hayas divertido.*

— *Dime, Lorenzo, ¿qué te gustó más de la ciudad?*

— *¿Qué tal tu español?*

Palabras y frases útiles

- *un partido de tenis*
- *un torneo*
- *la copa ecuatoriana*
- *el museo de oro*
- *las iglesias de la ciudad*
- *los parques*
- *las diversiones*
- *gustar*
- *preferir*
- *visitar*
- *ver*
- *caminar*
- *comprar*
- *divertirse*
- *pasarla bien*

Unidad 5

Situación 5

Situación

Luisa phones her friend Úrsula. She wants to give her two tickets for the Tornados concert on Friday night. The tickets for this popular rock group were sold out last month. Unfortunately, Úrsula has already made plans for that night.

Papeles

➡ **Luisa**
Úrsula
(dos amigas)

Conversación

You are Luisa. Tell Úrsula that you bought the tickets a month ago. Explain to her that you cannot attend because you have a wedding to go to in another city that day. Ask her if she knows anyone who would like to buy or use the tickets.

Sugerencias

— *Es Luisa.*
— *Te llamaba para saber si te gustaría ir al concierto . . .*
— *Tengo un par de boletos para . . .*
— *Pero tengo que . . .*
— *¿Conoces a alguïen que . . . ?*

Palabras y frases útiles

- *un par de billetes/boletos*
- *buenos asientos*
- *el concierto de rock*
- *el conjunto*
- *una boda*
- *el mismo día*
- *comprar los billetes*
- *pagar*
- *utilizar*

UNIDAD 5
Situación 5
A

Unidad 5

Situación 5

Situación

Luisa phones her friend Úrsula. She wants to give her two tickets for the Tornados concert on Friday night. The tickets for this popular rock group were sold out last month. Unfortunately, Úrsula has already made plans for that night.

Papeles

Luisa
➜ **Úrsula**
(dos amigas)

— Conversación —

You are Úrsula. Thank Luisa for offering you the tickets. Explain to her that you have already made plans for that night. Tell her that Roberto and José may buy them or use them.

Sugerencias

— *Te lo agradezco muchísimo . . .*
— *Me encanta la música de . . .*
— *Desgraciadamente tengo planes . . .*
— *Te sugiero que . . .*

Palabras y frases útiles

- *los billetes/boletos*
- *un concierto de rock*
- *el conjunto*
- *una boda*
- *tener planes*
- *no poder asistir*
- *ofrecer los billetes a*
- *comprar*
- *regalar*
- *utilizar*
- *pagar*

Unidad 6

Situación 1

Situación

Eugenio has just returned from a two-week cruise. He phones his friend Mónica to tell her all about the trip.

Papeles

→ **Eugenio**
Mónica
(dos amigos)

Conversación

You are Eugenio. Tell Mónica that you had a good time because you were able to rest and eat well. Tell her that the weather was good and that you went swimming and sunbathed every day. Ask her if she received the postcards you sent her.

Sugerencias

— *¿Qué tal?*
— *Acabo de llegar de . . .*
— *Quería contarte del . . .*
— *Hizo buen tiempo y . . .*
— *¿Recibiste . . . ?*

Palabras y frases útiles

- *regresar de*
- *dos semanas*
- *en un cruzero*
- *bañarse*
- *broncearse*
- *descansar*
- *disfrutar*
- *divertirse*
- *hacer buen tiempo*
- *tomar el sol*
- *marearse*
- *caerse al mar*
- *enviar/mandar postales*
- *divertidos*
- *entretenidos*
- *las postales*

UNIDAD 6
Situación 1
A

Situación

Eugenio has just returned from a two-week cruise. He phones his friend Mónica to tell her all about the trip.

Papeles

Eugenio
➡ **Mónica**
   (dos amigos)

Conversación

You are Mónica. Tell Eugenio that you received three postcards and that you know he had a good time. Ask him if he got seasick. Tell him that you took sailing lessons and you capsized a few times. Ask him if he is tanned or sunburnt. Tell him that now you have a nice tan.

Sugerencias

— *Recibí tres . . .*

— *Me alegro de que hayas pasado bien . . .*

— *Te mareaste . . .*

— *Tomé lecciones de vela y me caí al mar.*

— *¿Estás muy . . . o . . . ?*

Palabras y frases útiles

- *las postales*
- *el bote de vela*
- *recibir postales*
- *disfrutar*
- *divertirse*
- *hacer buen tiempo*
- *tomar el sol*
- *marearse*
- *caerse al mar*
- *broncearse*
- *estar bronceado*
- *divertido*
- *entretenido*

Unidad 6
Situación 2

〜〜〜〜〜〜〜〜〜〜〜〜〜〜〜〜〜〜

Situación

Paula is planning a camping vacation. She calls her friend Fernando, who does a lot of camping and hiking, to ask him for the best nearby place to go.

Papeles

→ **Paula**
Fernando
(dos amigos)

— Conversación —

You are Paula. Ask Fernando about the place he went camping last year. Ask if you can go mountain climbing in that area. Fernando will give you ideas to help you with your vacation plans.

Sugerencias

— *Es Paula.*
— *Fernando, te llamaba para que me sugieras el mejor lugar para acampar a unas dos o tres horas de aquí.*
— *¿Dónde . . . ?*

Palabras y frases útiles

- *¿puedes sugerirme . . . ?*
- *¿puedes indicarme . . . ?*
- *el mejor lugar*
- *un lugar para acampar*
- *ir de camping*
- *el campo*
- *practicar el alpinismo*
- *caminar*

Unidad 6

Situación 2

Situación

Paula is planning a camping vacation. She calls her friend Fernando, who does a lot of camping and hiking, to ask him for the best nearby place to go.

Papeles

Paula
→ **Fernando**
  (dos amigos)

Conversación

You are Fernando. Describe to Paula the place you went camping last year. Tell her that she can go mountain climbing in that area. Tell her to be careful when climbing boulders and rocks. Brainstorm and give her suggestions on what to pack. Warn her about possible fires.

Sugerencias

— *Te sugiero que vayas a . . .*
— *Es el mejor lugar para acampar.*
— *Queda a . . . de aquí.*
— *Ten cuidado con . . .*
— *Cuidado con poner fuego al . . .*

Palabras y frases útiles

- *el año pasado*
- *el lugar de camping*
- *acampar*
- *ir de camping*
- *el campo*
- *el lugar*
- *practicar el alpinismo*
- *tener cuidado*
- *caminar*
- *escalar*
- *trepar las rocas*
- *poner fuego al bosque*
- *perderse en la montaña*
- *resbalarse*
- *deslizarse*
- *llevar*
- *empacar*

Unidad 6

Situación 3

Situación

Octavio is talking to his friend Carlota on the phone. They are discussing last night's storm.

Papeles

→ **Octavio**
Carlota
  (dos amigos)

— Conversación —

You are Octavio. Tell Carlota that on your way home from work you were caught in the storm. Tell Carlota that you saw a bad accident on the highway. Explain that you think the accident was caused by the snow and ice on the road. Mention that, fortunately, the drivers were not injured.

Sugerencias

— *¡Adivina lo que me ocurrió!*

— *Cuando venía a casa empezó la tormenta . . .*

— *Vi un accidente muy serio en la carretera . . .*

— *Afortunadamente . . .*

Palabras y frases útiles

- *anoche*
- *la carretera*
- *los coches*
- *el tráfico*
- *había neblina*
- *había hielo*
- *había granizo*
- *una tormenta de invierno*
- *los conductores*
- *suceder*
- *ver*
- *no pasar nada*

UNIDAD 6
Situación 3
A

Unidad 6

Situación 3

Situación

Octavio is talking to his friend Carlota on the phone. They are discussing last night's storm.

Papeles

Octavio
➔ **Carlota**
 (dos amigos)

Conversación

You are Carlota. You listen to Octavio's story. Ask him where the bad accident occurred on the highway. Tell him that according to the news, the snow and ice on the road caused seven casualties. Mention that you were concerned about your father's commute home.

Sugerencias

— *¿Dónde fue el accidente que viste?*
— *Las noticias del Canal 5 dicen que la tormenta . . .*
— *El hielo y . . .*
— *Estaba preocupada por . . .*

Palabras y frases útiles

- *anoche*
- *la carretera*
- *serios accidentes*
- *a causa de . . .*
- *según las noticias de la televisión*
- *siete accidentes*
- *la neblina*
- *una tormenta*
- *el hielo*
- *el granizo*
- *los conductores*
- *suceder*
- *ver*
- *estar preocupada por . . .*
- *regresar a casa*
- *volver del trabajo*

© D.C. Heath and Company

UNIDAD 6
Situación 3

Unidad 6

Situación 4

Situación

Eliana and her younger cousin Luis are talking on the phone during an ice storm when Luis hears a very loud noise. He is home alone and is very scared.

Papeles

→ **Luis**
Eliana
(primos)

Conversación

You are Luis. Tell Eliana to wait a second while you look through the window to see what happened. It is cold and very windy outside. Tell Eliana that a tree branch broke and fell to the ground.

Sugerencias

— *Eliana, espera un minuto.*
— *Acabo de escuchar un ruido muy fuerte cerca del patio.*

Palabras y frases útiles

- *hace mucho frío*
- *hace mucho viento*
- *hay hielo*
- *hay una tempestad*
- *hay una tormenta*
- *nieva*
- *oír un ruido*
- *mirar por la ventana*
- *romperse*
- *caer al suelo*
- *la rama del árbol*
- *el patio*

Unidad 6

Situación 4

Situación

Eliana and her younger cousin Luis are talking on the phone during an ice storm when Luis hears a very loud noise. He is home alone and is very scared.

Papeles

Luis
→ **Eliana**
  (primos)

Conversación

You are Eliana. Ask Luis about the loud noise he heard. Inform him that a section of his neighborhood has had a blackout. Tell him not to be scared. Instruct him to find a flashlight. Talk about two things one should do during a storm.

Sugerencias

— *Luis, ¿qué causó el ruido en tu casa?*
— *En una sección de tu vecindario, hubo un apagón hace . . . y todavía no hay . . .*
— *Puedes ir a buscar . . .*

Palabras y frases útiles

- *estar solo en casa*
- *tener miedo*
- *estar asustado*
- *hace mucho frío*
- *hace mucho viento*
- *hay hielo*
- *oír un gran ruido*
- *una tempestad*
- *una tormenta de nieve*
- *un apagón de luces*
- *el vecindario*
- *lámpara de gas*
- *linterna*

UNIDAD 6
Situación 4
B

Unidad 6

Situación 5

Situación

Alberto and his friend Rodolfo are walking home from school on a Friday afternoon. They are discussing their plans for the weekend.

Papeles

→ **Rodolfo**
Alberto
(dos amigos)

Conversación

You are Rodolfo. Tell Alberto that you cannot go to baseball practice because you have to go to your sister's graduation in the morning. Afterward, the family is going to have dinner at a restaurant in the country. Ask Alberto what his plans are for tomorrow.

Sugerencias

— *Mañana por la mañana no puedo . . .*
— *Tengo que ir a la graduación . . .*
— *Después vamos a cenar a un restaurante . . .*
— *¿Y tú? ¿Qué piensas . . . ?*

Palabras y frases útiles

- *por la mañana*
- *faltar a la práctica de béisbol*
- *a causa de . . .*
- *la graduación*
- *después*
- *un restaurante*
- *el campo*

**UNIDAD 6
Situación 5
A**

Situación

Alberto and his friend Rodolfo are walking home from school on a Friday afternoon. They are discussing their plans for the weekend.

Papeles

Rodolfo
➔ **Alberto**
   (dos amigos)

Conversación

You are Alberto. Tell Rodolfo that if it does not rain, you plan to go hiking during the day with some friends. In the evening you and your family are having guests for dinner. Sunday you must study for an important test.

Sugerencias

— *Si no llueve, pienso ir . . .*
— *Por la noche mis padres tienen invitados para cenar . . .*
— *El domingo debo . . .*

Palabras y frases útiles

- *mañana por la mañana*
- *si no llueve*
- *caminar*
- *subir las montañas*
- *por la noche*
- *tener invitados*
- *el domingo*
- *un examen importante*

Unidad 7

Situación 1

Situación

Julia has stopped at a small grocery store on the way home from work. She needs to pick up the ingredients to bake a chocolate cake.

Papeles

➡ **Julia** *(cliente)*
Enrique *(empleado)*

Conversación

You are Julia. You are at the grocery store buying ingredients to make a chocolate cake. You need to buy a package of sugar, a dozen eggs, some butter, a liter of milk, and three bars of baking chocolate. Ask the clerk if there are any smaller packages of sugar. Ask him where the baking chocolate is.

Sugerencias

— *Por favor, ¿puede decirme dónde están los paquetes . . . y . . . ?*

Palabras y frases útiles

- *hacer un pastel*
- *ir de compras*
- *ir a la tienda de comestibles*
- *unos ingredientes*
- *un paquete de azúcar*
- *una docena de huevos*
- *mantequilla*
- *un litro de leche*
- *unas barras de chocolate*

Unidad 7

Situación 1

Situación

Julia has stopped at a small grocery store on the way home from work. She needs to pick up the ingredients to bake a chocolate cake.

Papeles

Julia *(cliente)*
➜ **Enrique** *(empleado)*

Conversación

You are Enrique. Inform Julia that you only sell sugar in 5-pound bags. Tell her where the baking chocolate is. Mention that eggs and sardines are on sale this week.

Sugerencias

— *Lo siento, pero todos los paquetes de azúcar son de cinco . . .*

— *Las barras de chocolate están en . . .*

— *Esta semana . . . a un precio especial . . .*

Palabras y frases útiles

• *hacer un pastel*
• *ir de compras*
• *ir a la tienda de comestibles*
• *estar de venta*
• *unos ingredientes*
• *un paquete de azúcar*
• *una docena de huevos*
• *mantequilla*
• *un litro de leche*
• *unas barras de chocolate*
• *precios especiales*

Unidad 7

Situación 2

Situación

Virginia works at the cash register in the "best" supermarket in Miami. Arturo, a customer, has stopped in to do some light shopping. He is at Virginia's register.

Papeles

➡ **Virginia** *(cajera)*
Arturo *(cliente)*

Conversación

You are Virginia. Tell Arturo, your customer, how much he owes you for one box of cookies, three cans of tuna, a bottle of milk, and a pound of butter. Tell him how much change you are giving him. Ask him if he wants his groceries in a paper or a plastic bag.

Sugerencias

— *El total de su compra es . . .*
— *Su cambio es . . .*
— *Le gustaría . . .*

Palabras y frases útiles

• *el total de . . .*
• *Ud. debe . . .*
• *la cuenta es . . .*
• *una caja de galletas*
• *una lata de atún*
• *una libra de mantequilla*
• *una bolsa de papel*
• *una bolsa de plástico*

Situación

Virginia works at the cash register in the "best" supermarket in Miami. Arturo, a customer, has stopped in to do some light shopping. He is at Virginia's register.

Papeles

Virginia *(cajera)*
➔ **Arturo** *(cliente)*

Conversación

You are Arturo. Tell Virginia that you have a discount coupon for the cookies. Pay Virginia for the groceries. Ask her for a paper bag. Find out the store's new hours.

Sugerencias

— *Mire, Srta., tengo un cupón de 50 centavos de descuento para las galletas.*

— *Y ahora, dígame, ¿cuánto es?*

— *¿Puede poner todo en . . . ?*

— *Podría decirme el horario nuevo . . .*

Palabras y frases útiles

- *un cupón de descuento*
- *una caja de galletas*
- *una lata de atún*
- *una libra de mantequilla*
- *una bolsa de papel*
- *una bolsa de plástico*
- *¿a qué hora se abre la tienda?*

Situación

Gloria is inviting her classmate Enrique to a dinner party. She is planning the menu and knows that Enrique is allergic to cheese.

Papeles

➔ **Gloria**
Enrique
(dos amigos)

Conversación

You are Gloria. You call Enrique to find out if he is allergic to anything other than cheese. You ask your friend about five other foods that he might be allergic to. Then work out a menu that he can enjoy.

Sugerencias

— *Aló, Enrique.*
— *Soy Gloria.*
— *Puedes decirme si eres . . .*

Palabras y frases útiles

- *ser alérgico a*
- *tener alergias a*
- *las aceitunas*
- *el arroz*
- *el atún*
- *los caramelos*
- *el chorizo*
- *las galletas*
- *los huevos*
- *el jamón*
- *la mostaza*
- *el queso*
- *las rosetas de maíz*
- *las sardinas*

© D.C. Heath and Company

Unidad 7

Estudiante B

Situación 3

Situación

Gloria is inviting her classmate Enrique to a dinner party. She is planning the menu and knows that Enrique is allergic to cheese.

Papeles

Gloria
➔ **Enrique**
(dos amigos)

Conversación

You are Enrique. Gloria calls you to find out if you are allergic to anything other than cheese. Let her know that there are three other foods you are allergic to. Help her work out a menu that you can enjoy.

Sugerencias

— *Gracias por la invitación y gracias por preguntarme si . . .*

— *Mira, yo no puedo comer . . .*

Palabras y frases útiles

- *ser alérgico a*
- *tener alergias a*
- *las aceitunas*
- *el arroz*
- *el atún*
- *los caramelos*
- *el chorizo*
- *las galletas*
- *los huevos*
- *el jamón*
- *la mostaza*
- *el queso*
- *las rosetas de maíz*
- *las sardinas*

Situación

Guido is at a vegetarian restaurant. Emilia is a waitress at the restaurant.

Papeles

→ **Guido** *(cliente)*
 Emilia *(mesera)*

Conversación

You are Guido. You are a true vegetarian. Ask Emilia what today's special is. Decide on a dish and order it. Add that for dessert you would like the peaches with honey.

Sugerencias

— *¿Puede decirme cuáles son
 las especialidades de hoy?*

— *¿Qué me sugiere como plato principal?*

— *¿Puede explicarme lo que es
 "Cornucopio de legumbres"?*

Palabras y frases útiles

- *¿cuál es la especialidad
 del día?*
- *¿cuál es la especialidad
 de la casa?*
- *me gustaría . . .*
- *para postre . . .*
- *el flan*
- *los garbanzos*
- *el guisante*
- *la zanahoria*
- *helado de chocolate,
 de vainilla*
- *la tarta de fresa*
- *la tarta de manzana*
- *la pera*
- *el melocotón*
- *con miel*

Situación

Guido is at a vegetarian restaurant. Emilia is a waitress at the restaurant.

Papeles

Guido *(cliente)*
→ **Emilia** *(mesera)*

Conversación

You are Emilia. Inform Guido of today's specials. After he orders, tell him that what he selected is a good choice. Comment that the peaches with honey are delicious.

Sugerencias

— *El plato de hoy es Cornucopio de legumbres.*
— *Es una tortilla grande de maíz con legumbres y salsa.*
— *Hay otros platos muy deliciosos en el menú . . .*
— *Lo que Ud. acaba de seleccionar es . . .*

Palabras y frases útiles

- *¿qué le gustaría cenar hoy?*
- *¿puedo ofrecerle los platos del día . . . ?*
- *el flan*
- *los garbanzos*
- *el guisante*
- *la zanahoria*
- *helado de chocolate, de vainilla*
- *la tarta de fresa*
- *la tarta de manzana*
- *la pera*
- *el melocotón*
- *con miel*

Situación

Sergio and his friend Jonathan work in the same office. Sergio is from Argentina and has invited Jonathan to dinner at *El Gaucho*, a well-known Argentinian restaurant.

Papeles

➜ **Sergio**
Jonathan
(dos compañeros de trabajo)

Conversación

You are Sergio. Tell Jonathan that the specialty of the restaurant is a "parrillada," a dish for two that comes with grilled steak, grilled veal cutlets, pork chops, and fried potatoes. Tell him that it is delicious and reasonably priced. Ask Jonathan if he would like to order the "parrillada" for two.

Sugerencias

— *Jonathan, ¿qué tal si probamos la parrillada?*
— *Es la especialidad de la casa.*
— *Es . . . y . . .*
— *Es abundante para dos personas.*
— *Tiene . . .*

Palabras y frases útiles

- *¿te gustaría probar . . . ?*
- *la especialidad de la casa es . . .*
- *es muy sabroso*
- *es de precio moderado*
- *el bistec*
- *las chuletas de cerdo*
- *las papas fritas*
- *sabroso*
- *a la parrilla*
- *el postre*

~~~~~~

Situación

Sergio and his friend Jonathan work in the same office. Sergio is from Argentina and has invited Jonathan to dinner at *El Gaucho*, a well-known Argentinian restaurant.

Papeles

Sergio
➜ **Jonathan**
   (dos compañeros de trabajo)

Conversación

You are Jonathan. You are dining with Sergio at *El Gaucho*. Agree to try the "parrillada." Ask Sergio if the dinner includes a salad, a vegetable, and bread. Discuss what you both want to drink with your meal and what dessert you might like to have.

Sugerencias

— *¡Claro que sí! Me encantaría probar . . .*
— *Tengo mucha hambre . . .*
— *También me gustaría pedir . . .*
— *¿Qué quieres tomar?*
— *¿Y para postre?*

Palabras y frases útiles

- *¿qué está incluido en la cena?*
- *¿qué te gustaría tomar?*
- *para postre me agradaría . . .*
- *el pan*
- *una ensalada*
- *las legumbres*
- *el bistec*
- *las chuletas de cerdo*
- *las papas fritas*
- *a la parrilla*
- *el postre*

Unidad 8

Situación 1

Situación

Cecilia is in the doctor's office.

Papeles

➜ **Cecilia** *(paciente)*
la Dra. Blanco *(médico)*

Conversación

You are Cecilia and you have an appointment with Dr. Blanco. Explain to the doctor that the cough syrup that you are taking is not helping. Tell her you think you might have bronchitis. Ask her to prescribe you something else. Inform the doctor of any allergies you have.

Sugerencias

— *No me siento bien . . .*
— *La medicina que me recetó . . .*
— *Pienso que tengo bronquitis . . .*
— *Solamente tengo alergias . . .*

Palabras y frases útiles

- *sentirse bien*
- *sentirse mal*
- *la medicina no tiene efecto*
- *el jarabe para la tos*
- *un caso de bronquitis*
- *una receta*
- *una pulmonía*
- *recetarle una medicina*
- *tener alergias a . . .*

Unidad 8

Situación 1

Situación

Cecilia is in the doctor's office.

Papeles

Cecilia *(paciente)*
➡ **la Dra. Blanco** *(médico)*

Conversación

You are Dr. Blanco. Cecilia, your patient, has told you that the cough syrup she is taking is not working. Tell her that you are going to take her temperature and blood pressure. You will also take an X-ray and run blood tests. Tell her that you think she probably has bronchitis.

Sugerencias

— *Me dices que el jarabe no tiene*
   ningún efecto.
— *Voy a tener que . . .*
— *Voy a recetarte . . .*
— *Pienso que tienes bronquitis . . .*
— *Dime, ¿qué alergias tienes . . . ?*

Palabras y frases útiles

- *sentirse bien*
- *sentirse mal*
- *la medicina no tiene efecto*
- *el jarabe para la tos*
- *un caso de bronquitis*
- *una receta*
- *recetarle una medicina*
- *examinar a un paciente*
- *tomar la temperatura*
- *tomar la presión*
- *tomar una radiografía*
- *hacer un análisis de sangre*
- *una pulmonía*

Unidad 8
Situación 2

Situación

Felipe has just returned home from the dentist's office. He tells his sister Lía about his appointment.

Papeles

➔ **Felipe**
Lía
(dos hermanos)

Conversación

You are Felipe. Tell Lía you were at the dentist's office for two hours because there was a blackout. Mention that the last time you visited the dentist you had no cavities, but that this time you had two. Tell her that the dentist recommended you brush after every meal and use dental floss daily.

Sugerencias

— *Imagínate que pasé dos horas . . .*
— *La última vez que estuve allí no . . .*
— *Esta vez el dentista encontró dos . . .*
— *Desafortunadamente, hubo un apagón y . . .*
— *El dentista sugiere que . . .*

Palabras y frases útiles

- *tener una cita*
- *pasar dos horas en la oficina del dentista*
- *una carie*
- *una inyección de novocaína*
- *el hilo dental*
- *la pasta dentífrica*
- *encontrar*
- *hallar dos caries*
- *rellenar las caries*
- *cepillarse los dientes*
- *reducir el riesgo de . . .*

Unidad 8

Situación 2

Situación

Felipe has just returned home from the dentist's office. He tells his sister Lía about his appointment.

Papeles

Felipe
→ **Lía**
   (dos hermanos)

Conversación

You are Lía. Tell Felipe that you have no cavities because you do not eat sweets. Mention that you visit the dentist every six months. Recommend to him a new brand of toothpaste and dental floss that you have seen advertised on TV.

Sugerencias

— *¡Qué lástima!*
— *Yo tengo mucha suerte, imagínate que la última vez que visité al dentista me dijo que no tengo . . .*
— *Visito al dentista . . .*
— *A propósito vi un anuncio en la televisión de . . .*

Palabras y frases útiles

- *una cita con el dentista*
- *una carie*
- *una visita cada seis meses*
- *no comer dulces*
- *el anuncio de la televisión*
- *una nueva marca de . . .*
- *el hilo dental*
- *la pasta dentífrica*
- *encontrar*
- *hallar una carie*
- *rellenar el diente/la muela*
- *cepillarse los dientes*
- *reducir el riesgo de . . .*

Unidad 8

Situación 3

Situación

Marcos is in school and he feels sick. He goes to see Mrs. Chávez, the school nurse.

Papeles

→ **Marcos** (estudiante)
la Sra. Chávez (enfermera)

Conversación

You are Marcos. You are coughing and sneezing a lot and you have a fever. You go to see the school nurse, Mrs. Chávez. Tell her that you have been taking cough syrup but you are not feeling any better. Tell her that you want to get well because you have a big football game this weekend.

Sugerencias

— *Me siento muy mal.*
— *Tengo mucha tos . . .*
— *Estoy tomando el jarabe pero . . .*
— *Creo que tengo fiebre . . .*

Palabras y frases útiles

- *sentirse mal*
- *tener mucha tos*
- *estornudar*
- *tener fiebre*
- *tomar un jarabe para la tos*
- *mejorarse*
- *tener un partido de fútbol*

Unidad 8

Situación 3

Estudiante B

Situación

Marcos is in school and he feels sick. He goes to see Mrs. Chávez, the school nurse.

Papeles

Marcos *(estudiante)*
➜ **la Sra. Chávez** *(enfermera)*

Conversación

You are Mrs. Chávez, the school nurse. Marcos describes his symptoms to you. Tell him that you will take his temperature. Recommend that he stay in bed for two days. Tell him that if he feels any worse, he should see a doctor as soon as possible. Advise him that unless he gets better, he must not go to the football game this Saturday.

Sugerencias

— *Marcos, me parece que estás muy enfermo.*
— *Déjame tomarte la temperatura.*
— *Te recomiendo que . . .*
— *Si no te sientes bien . . .*
— *Te sugiero que . . .*

Palabras y frases útiles

- *estar muy enfermo*
- *tomar la temperatura*
- *tener fiebre*
- *guardar cama*
- *hacer una cita con el médico*
- *mejorarse*
- *faltar al partido de fútbol*

© D.C. Heath and Company

Situación

Dr. Buendía is seeing Teodoro, a young man who has sprained his ankle badly in a skiing accident.

Papeles

→ **El Dr. Buendía** *(médico)*
Teodoro *(paciente)*

Conversación

You are Dr. Buendía. Ask Teodoro if he is in pain. Ask him where it hurts the most. Tell him that you are going to take an X-ray and that you will bandage his ankle. Mention the possibility that he will have to walk with crutches for at least a week. Ask him to see you next Friday afternoon.

Sugerencias

— *¿Qué tal, Teodoro?*
— *¡Un accidente de esquiar!*
— *Dime, ¿dónde te duele más?*
— *¿Sientes dolor . . . ?*
— *Voy a ponerte una venda . . .*
— *Vas a tener que caminar con . . .*

Palabras y frases útiles

• *¿cómo puedo ayudarte?*
• *dónde te duele más?*
• *tener dolor*
• *tomar una radiografía*
• *poner una venda en el tobillo*
• *caminar con muletas*
• *hacer una cita*
• *el próximo viernes*

Unidad 8
Situación 4

Situación

Dr. Buendía is seeing Teodoro, a young man who has sprained his ankle badly in a skiing accident.

Papeles

El Dr. Buendía *(médico)*
➜ **Teodoro** *(paciente)*

Conversación

You are Teodoro. Tell the doctor you are in excrutiating pain. Ask him if you have broken your ankle. Ask him to prescribe you medicine for pain. Ask him to tell you the things that you can and cannot do. Ask him how long it will be before you can return to your daily routine.

Sugerencias

— *Doctor, tengo tanto dolor que
     no puedo . . .*

— *El tobillo me duele . . .*

— *No tengo . . .*

— *¿Qué tipo de venda . . . ?*

— *Puedo . . .*

— *Debo . . .*

— *¿Cuánto tiempo . . . ?*

Palabras y frases útiles

- *tener mucho dolor*
- *torcerse el tobillo*
- *romperse el tobillo*
- *recetar una medicina*
- *para el dolor*
- *tomar aspirina*
- *poner una venda*
- *andar con muletas*
- *volver a la rutina diaria*

Unidad 8

Situación 5

Situación

Lucas is in the emergency room waiting
to be seen by Dr. Pizarro. He thinks he has
broken his arm in an ice-skating accident.

Papeles

→ **Lucas** *(paciente)*
la Dra. Pizarro *(médico)*

Conversación

You are Lucas. Tell the doctor you fell on your arm while ice skating
an hour ago. Tell her that it is very painful. Ask her if it is broken or
just sprained. Ask her what she is going to do.

Sugerencias

— *Hace una hora tuve un accidente
cuando patinaba.*

— *Me duele . . .*

— *¿Puede decirme si . . . ?*

— *Creo que . . .*

— *¿Qué me aconseja . . . ?*

Palabras y frases útiles

- *caerse*
- *resbalarse*
- *doler mucho*
- *fracturarse*
- *romperse*
- *torcerse*
- *vendar*
- *enyesar*
- *aconsejar*
- *una venda*
- *un yeso*
- *las muletas*

Unidad 8

Situación 5

Situación

Lucas is in the emergency room waiting to be seen by Dr. Pizarro. He thinks he has broken his arm in an ice-skating accident.

Papeles

Lucas *(paciente)*
➡ **la Dra. Pizarro** *(médico)*

Conversación

You are Dr. Pizarro. You ask Lucas for a detailed description of the accident. Ask him where it hurts the most. Inform him that he needs an X-ray so you can determine if the arm is broken or just sprained. Tell him he may have to have a cast. Indicate how long he will have to wear the cast.

Sugerencias

— *Dígame, ¿qué le pasó?*
— *Indíqueme donde le duele . . .*
— *Es necesario que Ud. . . .*
— *En una hora voy a saber si el brazo está . . .*
— *Creo que . . .*
— *Le sugiero que . . .*

Palabras y frases útiles

- *describir el accidente*
- *doler más*
- *tomar una radiografía*
- *fracturarse*
- *romperse*
- *torcerse*
- *vendar*
- *enyesar*
- *una venda*
- *un yeso*
- *andar con muletas*

Unidad 9

Estudiante A

Situación 1

Situación

El Corte Inglés, a department store, has just received a new shipment of short- and long-sleeve shirts. All employees have been instructed to promote the new shipment.

Papeles

→ **Marcela** *(empleada)*
Francisco *(cliente)*

Conversación

You are Marcela. You have been instructed to promote the new shipment of shirts. Tell Francisco, a customer, why you think these white cotton shirts are a real bargain. Have him try some on. Mention to him that the short-sleeve shirts would go well with both shorts and long pants. Point out the quality and practicality of the shirts.

Sugerencias

— *Hemos acabado de recibir estas . . .*
— *En mi opinión van muy bien con . . .*
— *¿Por qué no se prueba . . . ?*
— *Va a estar a la moda si . . .*

Palabras y frases útiles

• *acabar de recibir*
• *estar en oferta*
• *probarse*
• *ir bien*
• *¿de qué color le gustaría?*
• *es una oferta especial*
• *la camisa de algodón*
• *manga corta*
• *manga larga*
• *pantalones cortos*
• *pantalones largos*
• *el cuello*
• *los puños*
• *a la moda*
• *de excelente calidad*

Situación

El Corte Inglés, a department store, has just received a new shipment of short- and long-sleeve shirts. All employees have been instructed to promote the new shipment.

Papeles

Marcela *(empleada)*
➔ **Francisco** *(cliente)*

Conversación

You are Francisco, a customer shopping at *El Corte Inglés*, a large department store. Tell Marcela that you like the shirts; ask her if she has any white ones. Mention that you need a white shirt for your cousin's wedding. Ask her to help you find a tie to dress up the shirt. Discuss the color, size, and style of shirts and ties.

Sugerencias

— *Las camisas son muy bonitas y de buena calidad.*
— *Pero, dígame, ¿tiene Ud. camisas . . . ?*
— *¿Puede sugerirme una corbata que . . . ? Necesito . . .*
— *¿Qué le parece esta . . . con esta . . . ?*

Palabras y frases útiles

- *me encantan las camisas*
- *¿de qué color le gustaría?*
- *¿hay camisas blancas?*
- *una camisa blanca*
- *de manga larga*
- *el cuello*
- *los puños*
- *la boda de mi prima*
- *los colores*
- *las tallas*
- *el estilo de camisas y corbatas*

© D.C. Heath and Company

Unidad 9

Situación 2

Situación

Marlene and Octavio are out shopping for clothes.

Papeles

→ **Marlene**
Octavio
(primos)

Conversación

You are Marlene. Ask Octavio to try on a blue jacket. Tell him that it looks very good; it is the perfect size, color, and material. Tell him that he should buy it because it is the only one like it in the store. Inform him that the jacket is 20 percent off today. Suggest three places or events to which he can wear the jacket.

Sugerencias

— *Octavio, ¿por qué no te pruebas esa chaqueta . . . ?*

— *Te ves muy . . .*

— *Te sugiero que la . . .*

— *Es la única . . .*

Palabras y frases útiles

- *probarse*
- *ir bien con*
- *quedar bien*
- *la única de la tienda*
- *te queda bien*
- *de buena tela*
- *faltar dinero*
- *venta especial*
- *descuento*
- *colores:*
  - *marrón*
  - *negro*
  - *azul*
- *la chaqueta de algodón*
- *de lana*
- *la talla*
- *el estilo*

Unidad 9

Situación 2

Situación

Marlene and Octavio are out shopping for clothes.

Papeles

Marlene
➜ **Octavio**
  (primos)

Conversación

You are Octavio. You try on a jacket at your cousin's request. Explain to Marlene that you like the color and the material but that you do not really like the style. Tell her that you already have another jacket at home. Add that you don't have enough money to buy it. Mention two other pieces of clothing that you would rather buy.

Sugerencias

— *Me gusta mucho esta chaqueta azul y . . .*
— *No me gusta . . .*
— *Tengo una . . .*
— *Me falta dinero . . .*
— *Por ahora, prefiero . . .*

Palabras y frases útiles

- *me gusta mucho*
- *no me gusta el estilo*
- *me gustan el color y la tela*
- *me falta dinero*
- *me gustaría comprar*
- *acabar de probarse*
- *ir bien con*
- *quedar bien*
- *la venta especial*
- *el descuento*
- *los colores:*
  - *marrón*
  - *negro*
  - *azul*
- *la chaqueta de algodón*
- *de lana*
- *la talla*

Unidad 9

Situación 3

Situación

Elsa and her friend Anita are shopping for shoes at *Calzados Bellos*, a well-known shoe store.

Papeles

→ **Elsa**
Anita
(dos amigas)

Conversación

You are Elsa. You are looking for a pair of flat, comfortable shoes. You decide to try some shoes at *Calzados Bellos*. Ask Anita if the shoes you are trying on are in style and if the price is right. Ask her if she thinks you should buy them or not.

Sugerencias

— *Necesito un par de zapatos bajos de color negro, y quisiera comprarme un par de zapatos que sean . . . que tengan . . .*
— *¿Qué te parecen estos . . . ?*
— *Dime si están de moda . . .*
— *¿Y el precio . . . ?*
— *¿Qué me aconsejas . . . ?*

Palabras y frases útiles

- *voy a probarme . . .*
- *me quedan . . .*
- *¿qué me aconsejas . . . ?*
- *necesitar*
- *probarse*
- *calzar*
- *gustar*
- *quedar bien*
- *estar de moda*
- *estar a buen precio*
- *estar rebajados*
- *cómodos*
- *anchos*
- *estrechos*
- *de color . . .*

© D.C. Heath and Company

Unidad 9

Situación 3

Situación

Elsa and her friend Anita are shopping for shoes at *Calzados Bellos*, a well-known shoe store.

Papeles

Elsa
➡ **Anita**
   (dos amigas)

Conversación

You are Anita. Your friend Elsa asks you how you like the shoes she is trying on. Tell Elsa that you really like black leather shoes. Comment that the style is so-so. Mention that you do not like high heels or laces. Ask her if the shoes feel a bit too narrow. Advise her to go to another store.

Sugerencias

— *Me encantan los zapatos negros.*

— *Son de . . .*

— *Pero el estilo me parece . . .*

— *No me gustan los zapatos de . . .*

— *No me agradan los . . .*

— *¿Te quedan . . . ?*

— *Si no estás totalmente segura, te aconsejo . . .*

Palabras y frases útiles

- *me gustan . . .*
- *no me agradan . . .*
- *¿te quedan un poco . . . ?*
- *estar totalmente segura*
- *ir a otra tienda*
- *voy a pensarlo*
- *unos zapatos bajos*
- *unos zapatos de tacón*
- *de cuero*
- *con cordones*

Situación 4

Situación

Isabel and Vicente meet in a café after an afternoon of shopping. They talk about their purchases and how much they have saved by buying wisely.

Papeles

→ **Isabel**
Vicente
(amigos)

Conversación

You are Isabel. You are happy to see Vicente. Tell him that you bought a pocketbook, a necklace, earrings, and a bracelet. You also bought a scarf for your new black coat. Explain to him that you have a party and a family event to go to this weekend. Ask him to tell you what he bought.

Sugerencias

— *¡Qué cansada estoy!*
— *¡Ay, qué día!*
— *Mira lo que compré . . .*
— *Esta semana tengo . . .*
— *¿Y tú? ¿Qué compraste?*

Palabras y frases útiles

- *¡qué gusto en verte!*
- *¿qué vas a llevar . . . ?*
- *comprar*
- *ahorrar*
- *estar en liquidación*
- *estar rebajado*
- *tener una fiesta*
- *asistir a un evento familiar*
- *una bufanda*
- *una cartera*
- *un collar*
- *un brazalete*
- *unos pendientes*
- *un abrigo negro*
- *una cartera*

Unidad 9

Situación 4

Situación

Isabel and Vicente meet in a café after an afternoon of shopping. They talk about their purchases and how much they have saved by buying wisely.

Papeles

Isabel
→ **Vicente**
(amigos)

Conversación

You are Vicente. Tell Isabel that you bought a leather belt and a plaid shirt. Describe a winter sport jacket that you saw that you really liked. Tell her that you did not buy it because your parents are going to buy you a jacket of your choice as a birthday present.

Sugerencias

— *Bueno, yo no compré tantas cosas.*

— *Compré solamente . . .*

— *Pero ví una chaqueta de invierno fantástica . . .*

— *Es bastante cara, y yo sé que mis padres . . .*

— *Solamente tengo que decirles la talla y . . .*

Palabras y frases útiles

- *comprar*
- *escoger*
- *seleccionar*
- *un cinturón de cuero*
- *una camisa a cuadros*
- *una chaqueta deportiva de invierno*
- *un regalo de cumpleaños*

Unidad 9

Situación 5

Situación

Alejandro and Ramón are planning to go skiing next weekend. Alejandro calls Ramón to find out what he should pack.

Papeles

→ **Alejandro**
Ramón
(dos amigos)

Conversación

You are Alejandro. You call Ramón and tell him that you plan to take two pairs of corduroy pants, a pair of jeans, two wool shirts, an extra winter jacket, a pair of sneakers, and a pair of boots. Ask Ramón if there is anything else you need to bring.

Sugerencias

— *¡Aló, Ramón!*

— *¿Qué tal?*

— *Para este fin de semana, pienso llevar dos pares de pantalones de pana . . .*

— *¿Qué más debo llevar?*

Palabras y frases útiles

- *una estación de esquí*
- *el fin de semana*
- *unos pantalones*
- *unos bluejeans*
- *las camisas*
- *de pana*
- *de lana*
- *unos zapatos deportivos*
- *unas botas*
- *hacer mucho frío*
- *esquiar*
- *divertirse*

Unidad 9

Situación 5

Situación

Alejandro and Ramón are planning to go skiing next weekend. Alejandro calls Ramón to find out what he should pack.

Papeles

Alejandro
➡ **Ramón**
   (dos amigos)

Conversación

You are Ramón. Alejandro calls you about your skiing trip. Advise Alejandro to bring extra underwear and socks. Tell him to bring two sweaters, a hat, a pair of gloves, and a scarf. Ask him if he has an extra pair of sunglasses that you can borrow because yours are broken.

Sugerencias

— *¡Aló, Alejandro!*
— *Muy bien, ¿y tú?*
— *Creo que es suficiente, pero debes llevar extra ropa interior y . . .*
— *Dime, ¿tienes un par de gafas extra?*
— *¿Puedes prestármelas?*

Palabras y frases útiles

- *la ropa interior*
- *unos calcetines*
- *un suéter*
- *una bufanda*
- *unas gafas*
- *una boina*
- *una gorra*
- *unos guantes*
- *están rotas*
- *hacer la maleta*
- *prestar*
- *divertirse*

Situación 1

Situación

Carmen works as a ticket agent at Aerolíneas Argentinas. Emilio wants to buy a round-trip ticket to Argentina.

Papeles

→ **Carmen** *(agente de viajes)*
Emilio *(cliente)*

Conversación

You are Carmen, the ticket agent. Emilio wants to buy a round-trip tourist-class ticket to Buenos Aires. Tell him that if he stays a minimum of eight days he can get an excursion fare. Give him the price of the tickets. Inform him that the plane will make two stopovers. Ask him to show you his passport to confirm his ticket. Tell Emilio the flight number, the seat, and the gate he will be leaving from.

Sugerencias

— *Dígame, ¿en qué puedo servirle?*
— *El billete de ida y vuelta cuesta . . .*
— *El viaje de excursión cuesta . . .*
— *El avión . . .*
— *¿Necesita un . . . ?*
— *¿Puede mostrarme su . . . ?*
— *Aquí están sus billetes, el vuelo . . .*

Palabras y frases útiles

• *un billete de ida y vuelta*
• *un viaje de excursión*
• *hacer escala*
• *mostrar el pasaporte*
• *confirmar el billete*
• *el número de vuelo*
• *los asientos*
• *la puerta de salida*

Unidad 10

Situación 1

Situación

Carmen works as a ticket agent at Aerolíneas Argentinas. Emilio wants to buy a round-trip ticket to Argentina.

Papeles

Carmen *(agente de viajes)*
➡ **Emilio** *(cliente)*

Conversación

You are Emilio and you are buying a round-trip tourist-class ticket to Buenos Aires, Argentina. Ask the ticket agent for an excursion fare. Ask her if the plane makes any stops and if so, where. Show her your passport. Tell her that you are paying for the tickets with your credit card. Go over the flight schedule. Ask Carmen two more questions concerning your trip.

Sugerencias

— *Señorita, me gustaría comprar un billete de . . .*

— *¿Cuánto cuesta . . . ?*

— *¿Puede decirme dónde hace escalas . . . ?*

— *Deseo pagar con . . .*

— *¿Puede indicarme el . . . ?*

Palabras y frases útiles

- *hacer escala*
- *mostrar el pasaporte*
- *pagar con tarjeta de crédito*
- *un billete de excursión de ida y vuelta*
- *el horario de vuelo*
- *el número de vuelo*
- *los asientos*
- *la puerta de salida*
- *la hora de salida*

Unidad 10

Situación 2

Situación

Melania is in the train station. She has a long wait until her departure time. She asks Gregorio, a railroad employee, for some information.

Papeles

→ **Melania** (*pasajera*)
Gregorio (*empleado*)

Conversación

You are Melania. Ask Gregorio where the nearest newsstand is. Ask him if they sell magazines as well as newspapers. Ask him where you can buy a light snack.

Sugerencias

— *¿Puede decirme dónde queda un . . . ?*
— *¿Venden revistas . . . ?*
— *¿Qué más venden . . . ?*

Palabras y frases útiles

- *¿dónde queda . . . ?*
- *¿cuánto cuesta . . . ?*
- *un billete*
- *la entrada*
- *el puesto de revistas*
- *el quiosco de periódicos*
- *un café*
- *algo de comer*

**UNIDAD 10
Situación 2 A**

Unidad 10

Situación 2

Situación

Melania is in the train station. She has a long wait until her departure time. She asks Gregorio, a railroad employee, for some information.

Papeles

Melania *(pasajera)*
➜ **Gregorio** *(empleado)*

Conversación

You are Gregorio. Help Melania by giving her the information she requests. Tell her that the nearest newsstand is at the entrance to the train station. Mention that if she takes a right at the newsstand, she will see a café where they serve sandwiches and beverages. Tell her that there is also a gift shop next to the café. Inform her that there is a dining car in the train.

Sugerencias

— *Con mucho gusto.*
— *Mire, el . . . queda a . . .*
— *Si Ud. vira a . . .*
— *El café sirve . . .*
— *Al lado del café . . .*
— *El tren también ofrece . . .*

Palabras y frases útiles

• *¿dónde queda . . . ?*
• *¿cuánto cuesta . . . ?*
• *a la entrada de la estación*
• *a la derecha*
• *el puesto de revistas*
• *el quiosco de periódicos*
• *un café*
• *un sándwich*
• *unas bebidas*
• *algo de comer*
• *el tren comedor*

Unidad 10

Situación 3

Situación

Benito, a Mexican tourist, has just arrived at Barajas Airport in Madrid. He asks Alicia, the flight attendant, for information.

Papeles

➔ **Benito** *(turista)*
Alicia *(azafata)*

Conversación

You are Benito. You arrive at Barajas Airport and need information about where to go after deplaning. Ask Alicia, the flight attendant, where customs is. Also ask where the baggage claim area is. Ask her what the least expensive way to get to downtown Madrid is.

Sugerencias

— *Hágame el favor de indicarme qué debo hacer . . . ?*
— *¿Dónde está la . . . ?*
— *¿Cómo llego a . . . ?*

Palabras y frases útiles

- *¿qué debo hacer?*
- *¿cuál es la manera más económica de . . . ?*
- *pasar por la aduana*
- *ir a la sala de reclamación de equipaje*
- *tener el comprobante de equipaje*
- *pasar por la oficina de inmigración*
- *mostrar el pasaporte*
- *tomar transporte público*
- *pedir información en la oficina de turismo*

Situación

Benito, a Mexican tourist, has just arrived at Barajas Airport in Madrid. He asks Alicia, the flight attendant, for information.

Papeles

Benito *(turista)*
➔ **Alicia** *(azafata)*

Conversación

You are Alicia, the flight attendant. You help Benito find his way around the airport. Tell him where customs is. Remind him to have his luggage receipts ready when he goes to the baggage claim area. Suggest two inexpensive ways to get downtown. Direct Benito to the tourist information booth at the airport.

Sugerencias

— *Bueno, primero tiene que . . .*

— *Después vaya . . .*

— *Debe tener los billetes . . .*

— *Para ir al centro debe . . . o . . .*

— *A propósito hay . . .*

Palabras y frases útiles

- *permítame indicarle . . .*
- *la aduana queda . . .*
- *la sala de reclamación de equipaje queda . . .*
- *tener el comprobante de equipaje*
- *pasar por la oficina de inmigración*
- *mostrar el pasaporte*
- *tomar transporte público*
- *pedir información en la oficina de turismo*

Situación

Adriana, an exchange student, is flying from Barcelona to New York. Pedro, a flight attendant, is talking with her.

Papeles

➜ **Pedro** *(auxiliar de vuelo)*
Adriana *(estudiante)*

Conversación

You are Pedro, a flight attendant. Introduce yourself to Adriana and tell her that the plane will be taking off in 20 minutes. Ask her if this is her first trip to the United States. Explain that the flight will last six hours and that the plane will be flying over the Atlantic Ocean. Mention that a meal will be served in two hours. Ask Adriana if she has any questions.

Sugerencias

— *Soy . . .*
— *Este vuelo va a . . .*
— *El vuelo . . . y va a sobrevolar . . .*
— *Serviremos el . . .*
— *Si necesita . . .*

Palabras y frases útiles

• *me llamo . . .*
• *el avión despega . . .*
• *la duración del vuelo*
• *el auxiliar de vuelo*
• *el despegue*
• *la comida*
• *el océano Atlántico*
• *despegar*
• *durar*
• *sobrevolar*

Situación

Adriana, an exchange student, is flying from Barcelona to New York. Pedro, a flight attendant, is talking with her.

Papeles

Pedro *(auxiliar de vuelo)*
→ **Adriana** *(estudiante)*

Conversación

You are Adriana. Introduce yourself to Pedro. Tell him that it is your first flight overseas. Ask him if there is going to be a movie. Ask him for some magazines and for an extra blanket. Ask Pedro the time of arrival.

Sugerencias

— *Soy . . .*
— *Éste es mi primer vuelo a . . .*
— *Dígame si van a mostrar . . .*
— *¿Tiene . . . ?*
— *¿Puede darme una . . . ?*
— *¿A qué hora . . . ?*

Palabras y frases útiles

- *mucho gusto*
- *van a mostrar . . .*
- *el auxiliar de vuelo*
- *el despegue*
- *la comida*
- *una película*
- *una manta extra*
- *una almohada extra*
- *la hora de llegada*
- *despegar*
- *durar*
- *sobrevolar*

Unidad 10

Situación 5

Situación

Amelia is waiting for her train to Toledo. According to the schedule, the train was supposed to leave 30 minutes ago. Amelia approaches Andrés, the conductor, to find out what is causing the delay.

Papeles

→ **Amelia** *(pasajera)*
   Andrés *(conductor)*

Conversación

You are Amelia. Ask Andrés, the conductor, why the train has not departed. Ask him when the train will be leaving. Inquire about the time of arrival in Toledo. Tell him that you need to call your relatives to let them know that you will be late. Ask him where you can get a current train schedule to plan for your return trip.

Sugerencias

— *Disculpe, ¿puede decirme cuál es la causa del . . . ?*
— *¿A qué hora . . . ?*
— *Necesito llamar por teléfono a . . .*
— *¿Dónde puedo hallar un . . . ?*

Palabras y frases útiles

- *estar en retraso*
- *¿a qué hora sale . . . ?*
- *¿a qué hora llega . . . ?*
- *¿dónde puedo obtener . . . ?*
- *salir a tiempo*
- *llegar de retraso*
- *el horario de salidas y llegadas*
- *la oficina de información*
- *la taquilla*
- *el retraso*
- *un accidente*

Situación

Amelia is waiting for her train to Toledo. According to the schedule, the train was supposed to leave 30 minutes ago. Amelia approaches Andrés, the conductor, to find out what is causing the delay.

Papeles

Amelia *(pasajera)*

➜ **Andrés** *(conductor)*

Conversación

You are Andrés, the train conductor. Give Amelia two reasons why the train is not departing. Tell her the train will be leaving in one hour. Inform her that she can get a current train schedule at the information booth. Tell her that you do not think there is another direct train to Toledo today due to a strike in Madrid.

Sugerencias

— *Bueno, el tren no puede salir porque hay problemas . . .*

— *Estoy seguro de que . . .*

— *Si va a la oficina de información, encontrará . . .*

— *Dudo que haya otro . . .*

Palabras y frases útiles

- *estar en retraso*
- *a causa de . . .*
- *una huelga*
- *unos defectos mecánicos*
- *un accidente*
- *salir en una hora*
- *obtener el horario de salidas y llegadas*
- *ir a la oficina de información*
- *la taquilla*
- *el tren directo*

© D.C. Heath and Company

Unidad 11

Situación 1

Situación

Conrado, an amateur photographer, has just landed in Bogotá, Colombia, where he will spend the next three weeks taking photos for a wildlife magazine. He goes to the tourist desk and asks Dolores for some information.

Papeles

➔ **Conrado** *(fotógrafo)*
   Dolores *(guía de turismo)*

Conversación

You are Conrado. You are at the tourist information desk. Ask Dolores about inexpensive lodging near the historical district of the city. Mention that you are looking for a hotel near public transportation. Tell her what type of room you would like. Discuss the price and the amenities you would like. Ask her to make you a reservation.

Sugerencias

— *Srta., ¿puede darme información sobre alojamiento en . . . ?*

— *Quiero que quede cerca de . . .*

— *Me gustaría una habitación que tenga . . .*

— *¿Puede hacerme una reservación . . . ?*

Palabras y frases útiles

• *buscar alojamiento*
• *en el centro*
• *cerca del distrito histórico*
• *cerca de transporte público*
• *alojarse*
• *quedarse*
• *hacer una reservación*
• *llegar a*
• *cobrar*
• *por cuántos días*
• *hasta cuándo*
• *¿cuánto cobran por . . . ?*
• *un hotel barato*
• *de primera clase*
• *tipo de habitación*
• *barato*
• *cómodo*

UNIDAD 11
Situación 1
A

Unidad 11

Situación 1

Situación

Conrado, an amateur photographer, has just landed in Bogotá, Colombia, where he will spend the next three weeks taking photos for a wildlife magazine. He goes to the tourist desk and asks Dolores for some information.

Papeles

Conrado *(fotógrafo)*
➜ **Dolores** *(guía de turismo)*

Conversación

You are Dolores, a tourist guide at the information desk. Tell Conrado about two types of inexpensive lodging near the historical district of the city. Tell him that all of them are near public transportation. Tell him about the type of rooms available and their prices. Ask him which one he prefers. Make a reservation for him.

Sugerencias

— *Con mucho gusto. Hay dos tipos de alojamiento en el centro de la ciudad.*

— *El primero es . . .*

— *El segundo tipo es . . .*

— *Todos están cerca de . . .*

— *El precio de las habitaciones varían de acuerdo al . . .*

— *Unas habitaciones . . .*

— *Dígame, ¿cuál prefiere? Su reservación . . .*

Palabras y frases útiles

- *tipos de alojamiento*
- *unos hoteles*
- *unas pensiones*
- *quedarse*
- *hacer una reservación*
- *cobrar*
- *por cuántos días*
- *hasta cuándo*
- *¿cuánto cobran por . . . ?*
- *un hotel de primera clase*
- *un hotel de precio moderado*
- *los tipos de habitaciones*
- *la pensión completa*
- *la media pensión*

Situación

Dorotea, a tourist, has finally gotten into her room at the Hotel Isla Encantada in San Juan, Puerto Rico. She is very disappointed with the accommodations and she phones Luis, the hotel receptionist, to complain.

Papeles

→ **Dorotea** *(cliente del hotel)*
   Luis *(recepcionista)*

— Conversación —

You are Dorotea. You phone the hotel receptionist, Luis. Tell him that the bed in your room is not made and that there are no towels or hangers. Mention two other things that are missing. Explain that you are very tired and that you want a room that is ready now. Ask him to give you another room.

Sugerencias

— *Mire, lo llamo para decirle que la cama . . .*
— *Tampoco hay . . .*
— *Estoy rendida . . .*
— *Necesito . . .*
— *Haga el favor de darme . . .*

Palabras y frases útiles

- *la cama no está hecha*
- *faltan una cosas*
- *estoy rendida*
- *¿puede cambiarme de . . . ?*
- *hacer la cama*
- *una habitación limpia*
- *un cuarto listo*
- *la almohada*
- *la manta*
- *la percha*
- *la sábana*
- *la toalla*
- *el jabón*
- *la camarera*

UNIDAD 11
Situación 2

A

Unidad 11

Situación 2

Situación

Dorotea, a tourist, has finally gotten into her room at the Hotel Isla Encantada in San Juan, Puerto Rico. She is very disappointed with the accommodations and she phones Luis, the hotel receptionist, to complain.

Papeles

Dorotea *(cliente del hotel)*
→ **Luis** *(recepcionista)*

Conversación

You are Luis. Dorotea phones you to tell you that she is not pleased with the condition of her room. Explain to her that she was assigned that room by error. Tell her that she can change rooms or wait 20 minutes for the maid to do her room. Explain that today there were unexpected late checkouts and that the chambermaids were extremely busy. Apologize for the inconvenience.

Sugerencias

— *Lo siento muchísimo . . .*
— *Ha habido un error.*
— *El cuarto que Ud. tiene no está listo . . .*
— *Puede hacer una de dos cosas, esperar . . . o cambiar . . .*
— *Hoy ha sido un día . . .*
— *Muchas personas salieron . . .*
— *Por favor, disculpe toda la . . .*

Palabras y frases útiles

- *la condición de la habitación*
- *cambiar de habitación*
- *esperar unos minutos*
- *por error*
- *las camareras*
- *disculparse*
- *salidas tardes de los clientes*
- *la inconveniencia*

Situación

Isidro is the manager of the Vista al Mar Hotel. Constancia calls the hotel to make a room reservation, and Isidro answers.

Papeles

→ **Isidro** *(gerente del hotel)*
 Constancia *(cliente)*

Conversación

You are Isidro. You are on the phone with Constancia. List the three types of rooms the hotel has to offer. Ask Constancia what type of room she would like. Ask her how long she plans to stay. Tell her she may make a deposit by check or credit card.

Sugerencias

— *Sí, ¿qué tipo de habitación le gustaría?*

— *Ofrecemos tres tipos de habitaciones . . .*

— *¿Qué tipo de . . . ?*

— *¿Por cuántas noches . . . ?*

— *Para confirmar su reservación, necesitamos . . .*

— *Puede hacerlo con . . .*

Palabras y frases útiles

- *tipo de habitación:*
  – *un cuarto (doble–sencillo)*
  – *con vista al mar*
  – *con ventana a la calle*
  – *con baño privado*
  – *con ducha privada*
  – *con teléfono*
  – *con televisor*
  – *una reservación*
  – *la confirmación*
  – *los precios*
  – *el aire acondicionado*
- *hacer una reservación*
- *confirmar*
- *hacer un depósito*
- *pagar con tarjeta de crédito*

Unidad 11

Situación 3

Situación

Isidro is the manager of the Vista al Mar Hotel. Constancia calls the hotel to make a room reservation, and Isidro answers.

Papeles

Isidro *(gerente del hotel)*
→ **Constancia** *(cliente)*

Conversación

You are Constancia. You call the Vista al Mar Hotel to make reservations. Ask Isidro for a double room with a private bath and an ocean view. Inform him that you want to stay four nights. Tell Isidro that you want to reserve the room with your credit card. Ask three questions about the hotel facilities.

Sugerencias

— *Me gustaría . . .*
— *Quiero que tenga . . .*
— *Somos . . .*
— *Nos gustaría quedarnos cuatro . . .*
— *Quiero hacer la reservación con . . .*
— *¿Tiene el hotel . . . ?*

Palabras y frases útiles

- *una habitación doble*
- *con baño privado*
- *con vista al mar*
- *con ventana a la calle*
- *con teléfono*
- *con televisor*
- *una reservación*
- *la confirmación*
- *quedarse*
- *desde el . . .*
- *hasta . . .*
- *pagar con tarjeta de crédito*
- *¿puede decirme si el hotel tiene . . . ?*

Unidad 11

Situación 4

Situación

Mr. Maya, a businessman, is staying at the Hotel Fiesta. He is awakened by a phone call at 5:00 a.m.

Papeles

→ **El Sr. Maya** *(cliente)*
Margarita *(operadora)*

Conversación

You are Mr. Maya. You answer the phone. Tell the operator that she has made a mistake; you are not Mr. Jiménez and you did not request a wake-up call for 5:00 a.m. Tell her that you requested a wake-up call for 7:00 a.m.

Sugerencias

— *Aló. No, Srta., Ud. se ha equivocado.*

— *Éste no es . . .*

— *Es . . .*

— *No . . .*

Palabras y frases útiles

- *con el Sr. . . .*
- *lo siento mucho*
- *la llamada*
- *despertar*
- *una equivocación*
- *dormir*
- *pedir*
- *marcar*

Situación 4

Situación

Mr. Maya, a businessman, is staying at the Hotel Fiesta. He is awakened by a phone call at 5:00 a.m.

Papeles

El Sr. Maya *(cliente)*
➡ **Margarita** *(operadora)*

Conversación

You are Margarita, the hotel operator. You are calling Mr. Jiménez in room 308 because he requested a wake-up call for 5:00 a.m. The person that answers is not Mr. Jiménez but Mr. Maya. You realize that you dialed 380 instead of 308. Apologize to Mr. Maya for the error. Tell him that you will call him at 7:00 a.m.

Sugerencias

— *Aló, Sr. Jiménez, son las cinco de la mañana y . . .*

— *¿Cómo?*

— *Ud. no es el Sr . . .*

— *Lo siento mucho.*

— *Un momentito . . .*

— *Es un error.*

— *Me he equivocado.*

— *Debería haber marcado 380 y he marcado el 308.*

— *Disculpe . . .*

Palabras y frases útiles

- *con el Sr. . . .*
- *lo siento mucho*
- *la llamada*
- *despertar*
- *una equivocación*
- *dormir*
- *pedir una llamada*
- *disculparse*
- *marcar*

Unidad 11

Situación 5

Situación

Mr. Poveda is planning to spend four days with his wife in Sevilla. He phones to make a reservation at the Hotel Felipe II.

Papeles

→ **El Sr. Poveda** *(cliente)*
Arturo *(recepcionista del hotel)*

Conversación

You are Mr. Poveda. You call the Hotel Felipe II and Arturo, the receptionist, answers. Ask him to make a reservation for three nights, from December 12 to 14. Request a room for two people with a private bathroom. Ask Arturo how much the room costs per night and if breakfast is included in that price. Ask him if it is necessary to make a deposit to reserve the room. Ask him to send you a confirmation slip. Leave your address and your home telephone number in case of any changes.

Sugerencias

— *Aló, ¿con el hotel Felipe II?*
— *Quiero hacer una reservación . . .*
— *Nos gustaría un cuarto doble . . .*
— *¿Cuánto cobran por noche?*
— *¿El precio es media pensión?*
— *¿Es necesario que yo haga un depósito?*
— *En caso de cambio, mi dirección es . . .*
    o puede llamarme al . . .

Palabras y frases útiles

- *con el Hotel Felipe II . . .*
- *me gustaría*
- *quiero hacer una reservación*
- *por tres noches*
- *las fechas son . . .*
- *cuánto cobran*
- *un cuarto doble*
- *con baño privado*
- *hacer un depósito*
- *llamar*
- *llegar*
- *mandar una confirmación*

Unidad 11

Situación 5

Situación

Mr. Poveda is planning to spend four days with his wife in Sevilla. He phones to make a reservation at the Hotel Felipe II.

Papeles

El Sr. Poveda (*cliente*)

➜ **Arturo** (*recepcionista del hotel*)

— Conversación —

You are Arturo, the recepcionist at the Hotel Felipe II, and you answer Mr. Poveda's call. Inform him that you have entered into the computer his room reservation for two people with a private bathroom for December 12 to 14. Tell him the price of the room and mention that it includes breakfast. Tell him that is not necessary to make a deposit to reserve the room if he and his wife arrive before 4:00 p.m. Take his address and phone number and tell him that you will mail him a confirmation slip tomorrow. Thank him for calling the Hotel Felipe II.

Sugerencias

— *El hotel Felipe II, a sus órdenes . . .*

— *Sí, le he hecho una reservación para un cuarto doble, con . . .*

— *Cobramos . . . por noche.*

— *La habitación es media pensión y por lo tanto incluye el desayuno.*

— *No es necesario que haga un depósito si llega . . .*

— *Voy a mandarle por correo su confirmación de hotel.*

— *Le agradezco mucho que . . .*

Palabras y frases útiles

- *a sus órdenes*
- *le hago una reservación de habitación por . . .*
- *cobramos . . .*
- *necesitamos un depósito si llega . . .*
- *le agradezco . . .*
- *la habitación*
- *la confirmación*
- *llegar*
- *mandar por correo*
- *agradecer*

Unidad 12

Situación 1

Situación

Sara, a good friend of Marcos's, is moving into an apartment building in his neighborhood this weekend. Marcos is going to help her move. Marcos phones Sara to plan the move.

Papeles

→ **Marcos**
Sara
(dos amigos)

Conversación

You are Marcos. You call Sara. Tell her that you will be happy to help her move. Ask her to describe the apartment she is moving into. Ask her if she has a lot of furniture. Ask Sara three additional questions concerning the move.

Sugerencias

— *¿Qué tal, Sara?*
— *Me alegro de que te mudes en el vecindario.*
— *¿Puedo darte una mano con . . . ?*
— *¿Cómo es tu apartamento?*
— *¿Tienes muebles?*
— *¿Has alquilado un camión de . . . ?*

Palabras y frases útiles

- *alegrarse de que*
- *mudarse*
- *describir*
- *alquilar un apartamento*
- *alquilar un camión*
- *dar una mano*
- *el vecindario*
- *la mudanza*
- *los muebles:*
  - *de sala*
  - *de cocina*
  - *de comedor*

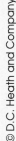
UNIDAD 12
Situación 1
A

~~~~~~

Situación

Sara, a good friend of Marcos's, is moving into an apartment building in his neighborhood this weekend. Marcos is going to help her move. Marcos phones Sara to plan the move.

Papeles

Marcos
➜ **Sara**
  (dos amigos)

Conversación

You are Sara. Tell Marcos what your new apartment looks like. Mention three things you like about the apartment. Say that you also like the neighborhood. Inform him that professional movers will move the heavy furniture but that you need help packing and unpacking clothes, appliances, and smaller items. Thank him for helping you move.

Sugerencias

— *Estoy encantada con el apartamento porque es . . .*

— *Me gusta mucho el . . .*

— *Una compañía de mudanzas va a . . .*

— *Necesito que me ayudes con . . .*

— *Te agradezco . . .*

Palabras y frases útiles

- *mudarse*
- *contractar una agencia de mudanzas*
- *dar una mano*
- *empacar*
- *desempacar*
- *agradecer*
- *la ropa*
- *los aparatos eléctricos*
- *los artículos pequeños*

Unidad 12

Situación 2

Situación

Matilda and Catalina share an apartment. Matilda has invited her office friends to dinner tonight. Catalina offers to help.

Papeles

➜ **Matilda**
Catalina
(compañeras de apartamento)

Conversación

You are Matilda. You are cleaning the apartment and preparing dinner when your roommate Catalina asks you if she can help. Ask Catalina to dust the living room. Ask her to set the table for eight. Tell her that the dinner will be outdoors. Decide on two more things that Catalina can help you with. Thank her for helping you.

Sugerencias

— *Gracias por darme una mano.*

— *Lo primero que quiero que hagas es . . .*

— *Me gustaría que . . .*

— *Vamos a comer . . .*

— *Si tienes tiempo, quiero que . . .*

Palabras y frases útiles

- *te lo agradezco*
- *vamos a comer afuera*
- *poner la mesa para ocho personas*
- *barrer*
- *sacar la basura*
- *sacar el polvo*
- *pasar la aspiradora a las alfombras*
- *la mesa*
- *las sillas*

UNIDAD 12
Situación 2
A

Unidad 12

Situación 2

Situación

Matilda and Catalina share an apartment. Matilda has invited her office friends to dinner tonight. Catalina offers to help.

Papeles

Matilda
→ **Catalina**
   (compañeras de apartamento)

Conversación

You are Catalina and you want to help Matilda with her dinner party tonight. Tell her that you will dust the living room and set the table. Mention that you will empty the trash. Offer to help Matilda with two more chores.

Sugerencias

— *¿Puedo sacarle el polvo a . . . ?*
— *¿Qué te parece si . . . ?*
— *Creo que debes . . .*
— *Debo llevar . . .*

Palabras y frases útiles

- *los periódicos viejos*
- *las revistas viejas*
- *poner la mesa para ocho personas*
- *barrer la cocina*
- *sacar la basura*
- *sacar el polvo a los muebles*
- *pasar la aspiradora a las alfombras*
- *la mesa*
- *las sillas*

Unidad 12

Situación 3

Situación

Nora tells her friend Salvador about the apartment she rented in Mexico City last summer. Salvador is planning to spend a year in Mexico City and wants to know more about the apartment.

Papeles

→ **Nora**
Salvador
(dos amigos)

Conversación

You are Nora. Describe your former apartment to Salvador. Tell him what electrical appliances were included. Mention three features you liked about the apartment. Inform him that the real estate management company asked the tenants to save energy by turning off the lights when they were not using them and to take the garbage out on Wednesday.

Sugerencias

— *El verano pasado . . .*

— *El apartamento tenía . . .*

— *Lo que más me gustó del apartmento fueron . . .*

— *La agencia de bienes raíces insistió que los inquilinos . . .*

Palabras y frases útiles

- *sacar la basura*
- *ahorrar energía*
- *apagar las luces*
- *no hacer ruido*
- *moderno*
- *espacioso*
- *soleado*
- *ventilado*
- *cómodo*
- *una refrigeradora*
- *el aire acondicionado*
- *la cocina*
- *el lavaplatos*
- *un triturador de desperdicios*
- *el garaje*
- *el ascensor*

UNIDAD 12
Situación 3 **A**

CONVERSEMOS   115

© D.C. Heath and Company

Unidad 12

Situación 3

Situación

Nora tells her friend Salvador about the apartment she rented in Mexico City last summer. Salvador is planning to spend a year in Mexico City and wants to know more about the apartment.

Papeles

Nora
➜ **Salvador**
(dos amigos)

Conversación

You are Salvador. Ask Nora if the apartment had a microwave oven and a garbage disposal. Ask her if there was anything she did not like about the apartment. Ask her two questions about the location of the apartment building in relation to downtown. Mention to her that for you it is important that the apartment be near the university and near public transportation.

Sugerencias

— *¿Tenía el apartamento . . . ?*

— *¿Dónde queda . . . ?*

— *Dime, ¿qué no te gustó . . . ?*

— *¿Había un . . . ?*

— *Para mí es importante que . . .*

Palabras y frases útiles

- *¿qué no te gustó del apartamento?*
- *es importante que . . .*
- *un horno de microondas*
- *un triturador de desperdicios*
- *el sitio*
- *cerca o lejos del centro*
- *cerca de la universidad*
- *con acceso a transporte público*

Situación

Tomás, a real estate agent, calls Pedro, a man who is interested in renting an apartment or a small house.

Papeles

→ **Tomás** *(agente de bienes raíces)*
Pedro *(inquilino)*

Conversación

You are Tomás. Tell Pedro you have a nice selection of apartments and small houses to rent. Ask Pedro if he would rather live downtown or in the suburbs. Ask him to list the amenities he wants. Ask him how much rent he is willing to pay. Ask him how long he wants to rent the apartment or house.

Sugerencias

— *En nuestra oficina tenemos una selección muy buena de apartmentos y casas.*
— *¿Le gustaría . . . ?*
— *¿Qué requiere Ud. . . . ?*
— *El alquiler . . .*

Palabras y frases útiles

- *tener una selección de apartamentos*
- *de casas pequeñas*
- *¿dónde le gustaría vivir?*
- *en el centro*
- *en las afueras*
- *moderno/antiguo*
- *pequeño/grande*
- *cómodo*
- *amueblado*
- *desamueblado*
- *con aire acondicionado*
- *el alquiler*
- *¿por cuánto tiempo quiere alquilar . . . ?*

Situación

Tomás, a real estate agent, calls Pedro, a man who is interested in renting an apartment or a small house.

Papeles

Tomás *(agente de bienes raíces)*

➜ **Pedro** *(inquilino)*

Conversación

You are Pedro. Tell Tomás, the real estate agent, that you would prefer to live downtown in an apartment building that is well ventilated and sunny. Tell the agent that the apartment must be in a modern building. Tell him that you would like to have laundry facilities in the building or in the neighborhood. Mention that you would prefer to rent a furnished apartment if the price were right.

Sugerencias

— *Me gustaría vivir en . . .*
— *Quiero un apartamento que . . .*
— *Preferiría que el edificio . . .*
— *Es necesario que . . .*
— *Lo ideal sería que . . .*

Palabras y frases útiles

- *en el centro de la ciudad*
- *en un edificio*
- *moderno*
- *antiguo*
- *pequeño*
- *grande*
- *cómodo*
- *ventilado*
- *soleado*
- *amueblado*
- *con aire acondicionado*
- *la lavadora de ropa*
- *la secadora*
- *la lavandería*
- *el alquiler*
- *estar a buen precio*

UNIDAD 12
Situación 4

B

Unidad 12

Situación 5

Situación

Chela has found a great job and she is moving to San Juan, Puerto Rico. She phones her friend Beatriz and asks for help selling her furniture.

Papeles

→ **Chela**
  Beatriz
    (dos amigas)

Conversación

You are Chela. Tell Beatriz that next week you would like to sell the sofa and all the extra cushions, the blue rug, the bureau with a mirror, the microwave oven, the freezer, the toaster, and a bathroom scale. Ask her to advise you about the selling prices. Mention two reasons why you have decided to sell these items. Ask Beatriz if she thinks you should also sell the armchair, the bookcase, and the desk. Mention to Beatriz that if she can use the curtains you will give them to her.

Sugerencias

— *¿Qué tal, Beatriz?*
— *Mira, antes de mudarme pienso vender . . .*
— *Necesito hacerlo porque . . .*
— *Dime, ¿qué te parece si . . . ?*
— *Bueno, si te sirven las cortinas te las regalo.*

Palabras y frases útiles

- *el diván*
- *los almohadones*
- *la alfombra*
- *el tocador*
- *un horno de microondas*
- *una congeladora*
- *una tostadora*
- *una báscula para el baño*
- *una butaca*
- *un estante*
- *las cortinas*
- *¿a qué precio?*
- *¿cuánto debo cobrar?*
- *pequeño*
- *grande*
- *incómodo*
- *pesado*
- *costoso*

Situación

Chela has found a great job and she is moving to San Juan, Puerto Rico. She phones her friend Beatriz and asks for help selling her furniture.

Papeles

Chela
→ **Beatriz**
   (dos amigas)

Conversación

You are Beatriz and your friend Chela phones you to inform you of her moving sale. Ask her how much she wants for each of the items she is selling. Give your opinion of the prices. Give a reason why she should not sell the microwave oven and the toaster. Tell Chela to sell the armchair and the desk and that you are interested in buying the bookcase. Say that you can use the curtains in one of your rooms and thank her for giving them to you.

Sugerencias

— *La venta de los muebles y de las otras cosas me parece una buena idea.*

— *¿Cuánto pides por . . . ?*

— *Si quieres vender . . .*

— *Si pides precios moderados . . .*

— *Te aconsejo que no vendas . . . porque . . .*

— *Es importante que te quedes con . . .*

— *Me intereso en el estante de libros . . .*

— *Claro que sí me encantan las cortinas, y puedo usarlas para . . .*

— *Gracias por dármelas.*

Palabras y frases útiles

- *un horno de microondas*
- *una tostadora*
- *una butaca*
- *un estante*
- *las cortinas*
- *pedir precios moderados*
- *interesarse en*
- *aconsejar que*
- *quedarse con*

Unidad 13

Situación 1

Situación

Yolanda is remodeling her bridal shop, and she phones Javier, an electrician, about some changes she needs made in the store.

Papeles

→ **Yolanda** *(dueña)*
Javier *(electricista)*

Conversación

You are Yolanda. You are phoning Javier, an electrician, to explain the work you need done. Ask him to check the fuses in the store. Tell him that you are going to need three additional electrical outlets. Ask him to check the batteries in all the store fire detectors. Ask him if he can recommend a good plumber because the faucet in the bathroom is not working properly. Mention that you would like the work done in the next two weeks if possible.

Sugerencias

— *Mire, quisiera que Ud. revisara . . .*
— *Voy a necesitar tres . . .*
— *¿Puede . . . ?*

Palabras y frases útiles

- *el enchufe*
- *los fusibles*
- *la pila*
- *los detectores de humo a pila*
- *el plomero*
- *el grifo*
- *funcionar*
- *reparar*
- *revisar*
- *instalar*
- *construir*
- *cobrar*

Unidad 13

Situación 1

Situación

Yolanda is remodeling her bridal shop, and she phones Javier, an electrician, about some changes she needs made in the store.

Papeles

Yolanda *(dueña)*
→ **Javier** *(electricista)*

Conversación

You are Javier, the electrician. Yolanda calls to hire you to do some work in her shop. Tell her what you charge for this type of work. Explain that you are also a plumber and that you can fix the bathroom faucet. Tell her you can do the job next week.

Sugerencias

— *Me parece que va a ser necesario que yo . . .*
— *Los tres . . . costarán . . .*
— *También soy . . .*

Palabras y frases útiles

- *el enchufe*
- *los fusibles*
- *la pila*
- *los detectores de humo a pila*
- *el plomero*
- *el grifo del baño*
- *funcionar*
- *reparar*
- *reemplazar*
- *revisar*
- *instalar*
- *cobrar por hora*
- *cobrar por trabajo*
- *empezar el trabajo*

© D.C. Heath and Company

Unidad 13

Situación 2

Situación

Andrés is going to buy his first car. He has found a four-year-old green convertible at a bargain price. He phones his friend Gerardo, a mechanic, to check out the car before he buys it.

Papeles

→ **Andrés**
   Gerardo
   (dos amigos)

Conversación

You are Andrés and you are planning to buy a used green convertible. Ask your friend Gerardo to check out the car. Ask him to meet you at Dan's Garage at 4:00 p.m. Give him directions to the garage. Ask him to take the car for a ride. You want to make sure that the engine is all right—you want to avoid breakdowns.

Sugerencias

— *Aló, Gerardo. Soy Andrés.*

— *Quiero que me hagas un favor.*

— *Pienso comprar un . . .*

— *¿Qué te parece si . . . ?*

— *¿Puedes conducirlo y revisar . . . ?*

Palabras y frases útiles

- *un descapotable*
- *la empresa "El automovilista"*
- *las señas*
- *las averías*
- *conducir el coche*
- *revisar la máquina*
- *arrancar bien*
- *levantar el capó*
- *revisar:*
  - *el carburador*
  - *las bujías*
  - *el radiador*

Unidad 13

Situación 2

Situación

Andrés is going to buy his first car. He has found a four-year-old green convertible at a bargain price. He phones his friend Gerardo, a mechanic, to check out the car before he buys it.

Papeles

Andrés
➜ **Gerardo**
   (dos amigos)

Conversación

You are Gerardo. Andrés calls you to ask you to check out the used car he wants to buy. Tell him that you will be delighted to test drive the car at 4:00 p.m. at the garage. Mention that you want to check the brakes and the engine. Give Andrés two things to look for or to avoid when buying a car.

Sugerencias

— *Está bien.*
— *Nos encontramos a las cuatro.*
— *Primero tengo que conducir el coche . . .*
— *Después voy a . . .*
— *Te aconsejo que . . .*

Palabras y frases útiles

- *conducir*
- *revisar los frenos*
- *las bujías*
- *el radiador*
- *las luces direccionales*
- *los faros*
- *las razones*
- *me parece que . . .*

Situación

Mauricio is a mechanic at a gas station. Benjamín, a customer, needs an inspection sticker for his car.

Papeles

→ **Mauricio** *(mecánico)*
Benjamín *(cliente)*

Conversación

You are Mauricio. Tell Benjamín that you need to check the brakes, the horn, the windshield wipers, the headlights, and the directional lights. Tell him it will be necessary to fix two things in order to get the new inspection sticker. Tell him the inspection fee is 15 dollars and the repairs are a separate charge.

Sugerencias

— *Necesito revisar . . .*
— *Tiene que hacer las siguientes . . .*

Palabras y frases útiles

- *la bocina*
- *los faros*
- *los frenos*
- *el parabrisas*
- *las luces direccionales*
- *el parachoques*
- *el capó*
- *arreglar*
- *reparar*

UNIDAD 13
Situación 3
A

Situación

Mauricio is a mechanic at a gas station. Benjamín, a customer, needs an inspection sticker for his car.

Papeles

Mauricio *(mecánico)*

➔ **Benjamín** *(cliente)*

— Conversación —

You are Benjamín. Tell Mauricio to do the necessary repairs so that you can get the sticker. Ask him how much the repairs will cost.

Sugerencias

— *Quiero que repares . . .*

— *Es necesario . . .*

Palabras y frases útiles

- *la bocina*
- *el carburador*
- *el faro*
- *los frenos*
- *el parabrisas*
- *las luces direccionales*
- *la inspección del coche*
- *costar*
- *reparar*
- *arreglar*

Situación

Beto has signed up for an auto mechanics class. Mr. Romero, his teacher, wants Beto to be an excellent mechanic. Beto wants to know everything possible about car repair because he wants to open his own business someday.

Papeles

→ **Beto** *(estudiante)*
el Sr. Romero *(teacher)*

Conversación

You are Beto. You want to know how to repair cars. You ask Mr. Romero how often one has to change the spark plugs in a car. You also ask him to teach you what to do in case of a flat tire. Ask Mr. Romero two more questions about car repair.

Sugerencias

— *Quiero aprender a reparar coches y . . .*

— *¿Puede decirme cuando . . . ?*

— *¿Qué hago en caso de que . . . ?*

— *Me encantaría aprender a reparar . . .*

Palabras y frases útiles

- *reparar un coche*
- *reemplazar las bujías*
- *revisar los frenos*
- *llenar la batería con agua*
- *mantener el nivel de aceite en la máquina*
- *cambiar el aceite*
- *llenar el radiador*
- *la goma*
- *la rueda*
- *la llanta pinchada*
- *el pinchazo*

Situación

Beto has signed up for an auto mechanics class. Mr. Romero, his teacher, wants Beto to be an excellent mechanic. Beto wants to know everything possible about car repair because he wants to open his own business someday.

Papeles

Beto *(estudiante)*
→ **el Sr. Romero** *(teacher)*

Conversación

You are Mr. Romero. You know that Beto wants to be a mechanic. Tell him how often to change the spark plugs. Tell him what to do in case of a flat tire. Name three things Beto must do to take care of a car.

Sugerencias

— *En caso de un pinchazo, tienes que . . .*
— *Para que un coche funcione bien, debes . . .*

Palabras y frases útiles

- *reparar un coche*
- *la goma*
- *la rueda*
- *la llanta pinchada*
- *el pinchazo*
- *la grúa*
- *la bocina*
- *el mantenimiento*
- *el aceite*
- *el agua*
- *la gasolina sin plomo*
- *la calidad de gasolina*

Unidad 13

Situación 5

Situación

Beatriz is in the appliance section of a large department store. She wants to buy a new stereo, but she does not know which one to choose. Agustín, an audio equipment salesperson, helps her.

Papeles

→ **Beatriz** *(cliente)*
Agustín *(vendedor)*

Conversación

You are Beatriz. Tell Agustín, the salesperson, that you are interested in buying a sound system that has a CD player and a cassette player. Tell him that you would like detachable speakers. Mention that you would prefer a double cassette player because you would like to do cassette mixing. Ask him what type of warranty is offered.

Sugerencias

— *¿Puede asistirme?*
— *Estoy buscando un equipo estereofónico que . . .*

Palabras y frases útiles

- *el equipo estereofónico*
- *el tocadiscos láser*
- *la grabadora*
- *la grabadora doble*
- *los altoparlantes separados*
- *el cassette*
- *un radio*
- *el sonido estereofónico*
- *de alta fidelidad*
- *garantía*
- *grabar*
- *preparar un cassette*

UNIDAD 13
Situación 5 **A**

Unidad 13

Situación 5

Situación

Beatriz is in the appliance section of a large department store. She wants to buy a new stereo, but she does not know which one to choose. Agustín, an audio equipment salesperson, helps her.

Papeles

Beatriz *(cliente)*
➜ **Agustín** *(vendedor)*

— Conversación —

You are Agustín, the salesperson. Tell Beatriz that you have five stereo sets that meet her needs. Mention that in two of them, the CD player is extra. Tell Beatriz that the warranty is one full year on parts only.

Sugerencias

— *Con mucho gusto.*
— *Tenemos cinco equipos estereofónicos como el que Ud. describe.*
— *Este . . .*
— *Ese . . .*
— *Aquel . . .*
— *Tengo uno que . . .*
— *La garantía es . . .*

Palabras y frases útiles

- *el equipo estereofónico*
- *los altoparlantes separados*
- *la grabadora*
- *el cassette*
- *el tocadiscos láser*
- *un radio*
- *el sonido estereofónico*
- *de alta fidelidad*
- *garantía de un año*
- *las partes solamente*
- *grabar*
- *preparar un cassette*

Situación

Mrs. Arredondo, a high school guidance counselor, is meeting with Felipe, a high school senior. They are discussing his plans for the future.

Papeles

→ **La Sra. Arredondo**
   (consejera)
   Felipe *(estudiante)*

Conversación

You are Mrs. Arredondo, the guidance counselor. Ask Felipe to name three fields or professions that he is interested in and to tell you why. Tell him about three different academic requirements or personal qualities needed for each of the professions he names.

Sugerencias

— *Dígame, Felipe, ¿qué profesiones o carreras le . . . ?*

— *¿Puede decirme exactamente por qué le interesa . . . ?*

— *¿Sabe Ud. que . . . ?*

Palabras y frases útiles

- *un abogado*
- *un arquitecto*
- *un dibujante*
- *un diseñador*
- *un periodista*
- *un representante de ventas*
- *un programador*
- *un contador*
- *la experiencia*
- *la paciencia*
- *la iniciativa*
- *los conocimientos técnicos*
- *las razones*
- *los requisitos*
- *las cualidades personales*

Situación

Mrs. Arredondo, a high school guidance counselor, is meeting with Felipe, a high school senior. They are discussing his plans for the future.

Papeles

La Sra. Arredondo
(consejera)
➜ **Felipe** *(estudiante)*

Conversación

You are Felipe. Tell Mrs. Arredondo that you are good with numbers and list the three professions that interest you the most and why. Mention that you would like to go to the Instituto Académico Nacional and ask her to tell you about the requirements.

Sugerencias

— *Sra. Arredondo, soy muy bueno con los números.*

— *Me encantan las matemáticas.*

— *Las carreras que me interesan más son . . .*

— *Me gustaría ser . . .*

— *Quizás me gustaría asistir a . . .*

— *¿Puede decirme exactamente los requisitos para . . . ?*

Palabras y frases útiles

• *un contador*
• *un programador*
• *un especialista de informática*
• *un profesor de matemáticas*
• *las carreras*
• *los requisitos*
• *ser buen estudiante*
• *tener iniciativa*
• *adquirir conocimientos técnicos sin dificultad*

Unidad 14

Situación 2

Situación

Patricia has started a new job as an assistant to Mr. García, an office manager.

Papeles

➜ **Patricia** *(asistente)*
el Sr. García *(gerente)*

Conversación

You are Patricia. Ask Mr. García, the manager, if you will have the opportunity to use the computer and the electric typewriter in your job. Tell him that you know how to work with computers very well. Ask him to list the things you must do every week. Tell him why you would like to have many responsibilities.

Sugerencias

— *¿Voy a tener la oportunidad de . . .
    y la . . . ?*
— *Sé usar . . .*
— *Hágame el favor de decirme lo que debo
    hacer cada semana . . .*
— *Deseo tener responsabilidades . . .*

Palabras y frases útiles

- *el gerente*
- *una máquina de escribir
  eléctrica*
- *una computadora*
- *tener iniciativa*
- *tener responsabilidades*
- *tener oportunidades de
  ascenso*

Unidad 14

Situación 2

Situación

Patricia has started a new job as an assistant to Mr. García, an office manager.

Papeles

Patricia *(asistente)*
➜ **el Sr. García** *(gerente)*

Conversación

You are Mr. García, the manager. Tell Patricia that she will have to use both the computer and the electric typewriter in her job. Mention that there is a new and efficient copying machine at the end of the hall. Name three things that need to be done every Friday. Tell her that you are delighted to know that she likes to have many responsibilities because this will give her opportunities for promotion.

Sugerencias

— *Tiene que usar la . . . y . . .*
— *Es nueva y muy eficiente . . .*
— *La nueva copiadora . . .*
— *Me alegro de que . . . porque entonces tendrá . . .*

Palabras y frases útiles

- *una computadora*
- *una máquina de escribir eléctrica*
- *una fotocopiadora*
- *los viernes*
- *tener iniciativa*
- *tener responsabilidades*
- *tener oportunidades de ascenso*
- *archivar*
- *programar*
- *hacer fotocopias*
- *al final del pasillo*
- *las copias*
- *los archivos*

© D.C. Heath and Company

Unidad 14

Situación 3

Situación

Gabriel and Laurita, two guests at a dinner party, are having a conversation about how they came to know their hosts, Pablo and Lucía Machado.

Papeles

→ **Gabriel**
Laurita
(dos invitados)

— Conversación —

You are Gabriel. Tell Laurita that you and Pablo went to the same high school and the same college. Mention that you majored in finance and Pablo majored in management. Explain that now you are both executives at the same insurance company. Mention that you work in different departments. Ask Laura how she knows Pablo and Lucía.

Sugerencias

— *Conozco a Pablo desde hace mucho tiempo.*

— *Asistimos a . . . y a . . .*

— *Pablo se especializó en . . .*

— *Ahora trabajamos para . . .*

— *Estamos en . . .*

— *Y dígame, ¿cómo conoce a . . . ?*

Palabras y frases útiles

• *graduados de la academia, de la universidad*

• *especializarse en finanzas, en administración de empresas*

• *la compañía de seguros*

• *un(a) ejecutivo(a)*

• *el departamento*

Unidad 14

Estudiante B

Situación 3

~~~~~~~~~~~~~~~~~~~~~~~~~~~~~~~~~

Situación

Gabriel and Laurita, two guests at a dinner party, are having a conversation about how they came to know their hosts, Pablo and Lucía Machado.

Papeles

Gabriel
➔ **Laurita**
    (dos invitados)

Conversación

You are Laurita. Tell Gabriel that you met Lucía in a computer science class in college. Tell him that you recently started a new job in an advertising firm. Mention that you did not realize that Lucía worked for the same company until a few weeks ago when you saw her at a sales meeting.

Sugerencias

— *Es una historia muy larga.*
— *Conocí a Lucía en una clase de . . .*
— *Hace tres meses tuve una entrevista con . . .*
— *Nunca supe que Lucía trabajaba para . . . hasta que la vi en . . .*

Palabras y frases útiles

- *una clase de informática*
- *la universidad*
- *una reunión de vendedores*
- *el departmento de ventas*
- *una agencia de publicidad*
- *conseguir un empleo*
- *darse cuenta de . . .*
- *asistir a una reunión de ventas*
- *encontrarse con . . .*
- *hace unas semanas . . .*